BLACK HUMOR

Terry Southern introduces us to a nine-year-old bootlegger and the twirling nymphets of the Dixie National Baton Twirling Institute.

John Rechy attends a hilarious transvestite orgy.

Thomas Pynchon contributes one of the drollest seduction scenes in all fiction.

Edward Albee dramatizes the eerie death watch of a daughter and a son-in-law.

Vladimir Nabokov delves into the strange affair of a Siamese twin.

John Barth immortalizes the rib-splitting encounter between Ebenezer, the virgin poet, and a very unusual whore.

AND MORE, MORE, MORE OF THE WICKEDEST COMEDY EVER PERPETRATED ON THE AMERICAN SCENE!

Black Humor

Edited by
BRUCE JAY FRIEDMAN

BANTAM BOOKS · TORONTO · NEW YORK · LONDON

BLACK HUMOR
A Bantam Book / published August 1965

Acknowledgments

Edward Albee: "The Sandbox." From The Zoo Story, The Sandbox and The Death of Bessie Smith, © 1960 by Edward Albee. Reprinted by permission of Coward-McCann, Inc. Notice: this play is the sole property of the author and is fully protected by copyright. It may not be acted by professionals or by amateurs without written consent. Public readings and radio or television broadcasts are likewise forbidden. All inquiries concerning rights should be addressed to the author's agent, the William Morris Agency, 1740 Broadway, New York, N. Y. 10019.

John Barth: from The Sot-Weed Factor, Copyright © 1960 by John Barth. Reprinted by permission of Doubleday & Company, Inc.

Louis-Ferdinand Céline: from Journey to the End of the Night. Copyright, 1934, by Louis-Ferdinand Céline. Reprinted by permission of the publishers, New Directions, New York.

J. P Donleavy: from The Ginger Man, © J. P. Donleavy 1956. ·

Bruce Jay Friedman: "Black Angels," © 1964 by Bruce Jay Friedman. "Black Angels" originally appeared in ESQUIRE.

Joseph Heller: "Milo," Copyright © 1965, 1961, by Joseph Heller.

Conrad Knickerbocker: "Pay Day," © 1964 by Conrad Knickerbocker. "Pay Day" originally appeared in THE PARIS REVIEW.

Vladimir Nabokov: "Scenes from the Life of a Double Monster," Copyright, 1958, by Vladimir Nabokov.

James Purdy: "Don't Call Me by My Right Name." From Color of Darkness, Copyright © 1956 by The Andreas Foundation, Copyright © 1957 by James Purdy. Reprinted by permission of the publishers, New Directions, New York.

Thomas Pynchon: "In Which Esther Gets a Nose Job," © 1963 by Thomas Pynchon.

John Rechy: "Miss Destiny: The Fabulous Wedding." From City of Night, Copyright © 1963 by John Rechy. Published by Grove Press, Inc.

Charles Simmons: from Powdered Eggs, Copyright © 1964 by Charles Simmons. Reprinted by permission of E. P. Dutton & Co., Inc.

Terry Southern: "Twirling at Ole Miss," Copyright © 1963 by Terry Southern.

Bantam Books are published by Bantam Books, Inc., a subsidiary of Grosset & Dunlap, Inc. Its trade-mark, consisting of the words "Bantam Books" and the portrayal of a bantam, is registered in the United States Patent Office and in other countries. Marca Registrada. Bantam Books, Inc., 271 Madison Avenue, New York, N. Y. 10016.

CONTENTS

FOREWORD

It is called "Black Humor" and I think I would have more luck defining an elbow or a corned-beef sandwich. I am not, for one thing, even sure it is black. It might be fuchsia or eggshell and now that I look at the table of contents I think some of it is in brown polka dots. My story, for example, is a brilliant midnight blue with matching ruffles around the edges. I certainly know what color it is since I did the coloring on this one myself and did not bring in a decorator as is my usual custom.

I am not sure of very much and I think it is true of the writers in this volume that they are not sure of very much either. They have some pretty strong notions, however, and one of mine is that the work under discussion, if not black, is some fairly dark-hued color. The humor part of the definition is probably accurate although I doubt that the writers here are bluff and hearty joke-tellers who spend a lot of time at discotheques. Invite them all to a party and you would probably find a great deal of brooding and sulking. At no time during the evening would they circle round the piano to sing hit tunes from Jerome Kern musicals. I think there would be many furtive glances about the room, each writer eyeing his neighbor suspiciously. One might suddenly fly through an open window, but only after carefully checking to see that the drop was shallow. For all I know one might seize another and cane him soundly about the shoulders as George Washington did to irreverent newspaper editors. They might all begin to cry, although I don't think so, for if there is a despair in this work, it is a tough, resilient brand and might very well end up in a Faulknerian horselaugh.

There would, in other words, be a certain resistance to the idea of lumping together thirteen writers with thirteen separate, completely private and unique visions, who in so many ways have nothing at all to do with one another and would not know or perhaps even understand one another's work if they tripped over it. And it is true that when you read through the work, it is, on the one hand, the separateness that strikes you as much as the similarity. You have storytellers in the old tradition here and you have others who will tell you to take your plot machinery and stick it in your ear. You have writers who know exactly what they are doing and others who do not have the faintest idea and are finding out in rather brilliant fashion as they go along. You have John Barth coming at you out of the late seventeenth century, J. P. Donleavy working his way through some insanely beautiful Irish song and Nabokov demoniacally using muscles no one else is blessed with. There is Thomas Pynchon appearing out of nowhere with a vision so contemporary it makes your nose bleed and there is Celine who reminds you that he thought all your thoughts, worked the same beat, was dumbfounded as many times a day as you are, long before you were born.

So you have thirteen separate writers who could not care less about one another and are certainly not going to attend any bi-monthly meetings to discuss policy and blackball new members. But there are some similarities, some stubborn echoes bouncing from one to the other, and I had better hurry up and outline them or else the anthology is over and everyone has to go home and nobody gets to make a buck.

You hear an awful lot about the "fading line between fantasy and reality" in the modern world and I had better put that in fast or else I am not going to get to do any more Forewords. So here it comes. I agree. There *is* a fading line between fantasy and reality, a very fading line, a goddamned, almost invisible line and you will find that notion riding through all of the selections in this volume. Then, too, if you are alive today, and stick your head out of doors now and then, you know that there is a nervousness, a tempo, a near-hysterical new beat in the air, a punishing isolation and loneliness of a strange, frenzied new kind. It is in the music and the talk and the films and the theater and it is in the prose style of Joe Heller and Terry Southern. You can find it in Gogol and Isaac Babel, too, and perhaps they saw it all coming. But that is another anthology.

These are fairly tangential considerations and what it really comes down to is *The New York Times*, which is the source and fountain and bible of black humor. The Secre-

tary of State, solemnly reviewing the Vietnam crisis, suddenly
begins to strangle on a wild gastronomical metaphor.
Hanoi's support of the rebels, that's the "meat and potatoes
issues." When we get to the root of that, then we can consider the salt and pepper issues. The bombing raids? Sec-
ondary stuff, just a lot of garlic and oregano talk, really,
just a bunch of diversionary sweet basil and East Indian nut-
meg baloney.

A ninety-year-old Negro sharecropper lady watches Lady-
bird Johnson—on a poverty-inspection tour—sweep up to
her shack in a presidential limousine and says, "Ain't it wonderful." Fun-loving Tennessee students pelt each other with
snowballs and suddenly scores are dead of heart attacks and
gunshot wounds. A mid-flight heart-attack victim is removed
from an airliner, suddenly slides from the stretcher and
cracks her head on the runway. We bomb North Vietnam
and nervously await the reaction of Red China, scourge of
the Free World. Red China breaks her silence. The Imperial-
ist dogs have behaved like vermin and Communist China is
not going to sit idly by. With all the fury and power of a
frenzied 900-million populace behind her, Red China speaks.

"We are going," says Radio China, "to return you tit for
tat."

You guess that it has always been this way, that Tolstoi
must have had this unreal sensation when Napoleon came
east. But then the police Urinary Squad swoops down and
spears a high governmental official at the Y.M.C.A. trough;
five hundred captured Congo rebels are ushered into a sta-
dium before their Free World captors. The ones who are
booed have their heads blown off. Those with good acts who
draw applause go free; Nehru sends troops rushing up to the
India-China border "with orders to shout if necessary."

"How does it feel?" the TV boys ask Mrs. Malcolm X
when her husband is assassinated. We send our planes off
for nice, easygoing, not-too-tough bombing raids on North
Vietnam. Sixteen U.S. officers in Germany fly through the
night in Klansmen robes burning fiery crosses and are
hauled before their commanding officer to .be reprimanded
for "poor judgment." It confirms your belief that a new, Jack
Rubyesque chord of absurdity has been struck in the land,
that there is a new mutative style of behavior afoot, one
that can only be dealt with by a new, one-foot-in-the-asylum
style of fiction.

If you are fond of pinning labels on generations, I wonder whether this one could not be called the surprise-proof generation. What might possibly surprise America? Another presidential assassination. Kidstuff. A thousand Red Chinese landing on the Lever Brothers building and marching toward Times Square. Hardly worth a yawn. Mike Todd suddenly showing up on the Johnny Carson show, not dead after all, involved in Broadway's greatest hoax. It's sort of expected.

What has happened is that the satirist has had his ground usurped by the newspaper reporter. The journalist, who, in the year 1964, must cover the ecumenical debate on whether Jews, on the one hand, are still to be known as Christ-killers, or, on the other hand are to be let off the hook, is certainly today's satirist. The novelist-satirist, with no real territory of his own to roam, has had to discover new land, invent a new currency, a new set of filters, has had to sail into darker waters somewhere out beyond satire and I think this is what is meant by black humor.

So you have Mrs. Liuzzo dead with a bullet in her brain, the federal government swinging into action because her "civil rights have been violated." The New York Police Department steps forth with a plan to keep Puerto Ricans from committing suicide in their cells: guards are to watch them like hawks now, running in to cut them down before they get their nooses rigged up. A news magazine says what's all the fuss about anyhow and describes one of our Vietnam gases as "fragrant-smelling," the implication being that if the little Red bastards weren't so sneaky, hiding in caves, we would not have to use gas in the first place. In one of our states, the penalty for fornication is six-to-seven years in prison while fellatio people (with only one pair of genitals involved) are imprisoned for life. It may be said that the Black Humorist is a kind of literary Paul Revere, a fellow who unfreezes his mind, if only for a moment and says, "For Christ's sake, what in hell is going on here? What do you mean, 35,000 Vietnam *advisers*?"

They say it is a critic's phrase, Black Humor, and that whatever it is, you can count on it to fizzle after a bit. And besides, don't these fellows just write about outcasts? Fags, junkies, hunchbacks, "preverts," Negroes, Jews, other assorted losers? What's that got to do with anything anyway? I think they may be wrong on that first count. I have a hunch Black Humor has probably always been around, always will be around, under some name or other, as long as there are disguises to be peeled back, as long as there are thoughts no one else cares to think. And as to the idea that these writers do not deal with "representative" types—it may be that you can govern by consensus, but you can't write anything distinctive by consensus. And it may be that if you are doing anything as high-minded as examining society, the very best way to go about it is by examining first its throwaways, the ones who can't or won't keep in step (in step with what?). And who knows? Perhaps "bad" behavior of a certain kind is better than "good" behavior. The American Health Society claims that only 5% of syphilis is spread by prostitutes.

So there is a Black Humor, after all, although you wish they would call it something else or perhaps call it nothing and just know it is in the air. Especially since there is no single perfect example of it, the way you can produce a perfect Uppman cigar. What is true is that the serious and effective social critics—the novelists, film makers, playwrights, the Feiffer-Krassner-Bruce axis—are working through humor; there is also an awful lot of questioning these days, some of it despairing, bleary-eyed, bedazzled, some of it young, vigorous, outrageous. And a group of novelists, very often working obliquely, coming at you from somewhere in left field, throwing you some laughs to get you to lower your guard, have decided that the novel is the proper place to open every door, to follow every labyrinthian corridor to its source, to ask the final questions, turn over the last rock, to take a preposterous world by the throat and say okay, be preposterous, but also make damned sure you explain yourself.

It is a good time to be around, to ask some of the questions, to watch the action.

BRUCE JAY FRIEDMAN

New York City
March 1965

BLACK HUMOR

THOMAS PYNCHON

In Which Esther Gets a Nose Job

Next evening, prim and nervous-thighed in a rear seat of the crosstown bus, Esther divided her attention between the delinquent wilderness outside and a paperback copy of *The Search for Bridey Murphy*. This book had been written by a Colorado businessman to tell people there was life after death. In its course he touched upon metempsychosis, faith healing, extrasensory perception and the rest of a weird canon of twentieth-century metaphysics we've come now to associate with the city of Los Angeles and similar regions.

The bus driver was of the normal or placid crosstown type; having fewer traffic lights and stops to cope with than the up-and-downtown drivers, he could afford to be genial. A portable radio hung by his steering wheel, tuned to WQXR. Tchaikovsky's Romeo and Juliet Overture flowed syrupy around him and his passengers. As the bus crossed Columbus Avenue, a faceless delinquent heaved a rock at it. Cries in Spanish ascended to it out of the darkness. A report which could have been either a backfire or a gunshot sounded a few blocks downtown. Captured in the score's black symbols, given life by vibrating air columns and strings, having taken passage through transducers, coils, capacitors and tubes to a shuddering paper cone, the eternal drama of love and death continued to unfold entirely disconnected from this evening and place.

The bus entered the sudden waste country of Central Park. Out there, Esther knew, up and downtown, they would be going at it under bushes; mugging, raping, killing. She, her world, knew nothing of the square confines of the Park after sundown. It was reserved as if by convenant for cops, delinquents and all manner of deviates.

Suppose she were telepathic, and could tune in on what was going on out there. She preferred not to think about it. There would be power in telepathy, she thought, but much pain. And someone else might tap your own mind without your knowing. (Had Rachel been listening on the phone extension?)

She touched the tip of her new nose delicately, in secret: a mannerism she'd developed just recently. Not so much to point it out to whoever might be watching as to make sure it was still there. The bus came out of the park onto the safe, bright East Side, into the lights of Fifth Avenue. They reminded her to go shopping tomorrow for a dress she'd seen, $39.95 at Lord and Taylor, which he would like.

What a brave girl I am, she trilled to herself, coming through so much night and lawlessness to visit My Lover.

She got off at First Avenue and tap-tapped along the sidewalk, facing uptown and perhaps some dream. Soon she turned right, began to fish in her purse for a key. Found the door, opened, stepped inside. The front rooms were all deserted. Beneath the mirror, two golden imps in a clock danced the same unsyncopated tango they'd always danced. Esther felt at home. Behind the operating room (a sentimental glance sideways through the open door toward the table on which her face had been altered) was a small chamber, in it a bed. He lay, head and shoulders circled by the intense halo of a paraboloid reading light. His eyes opened to her, her arms to him.

"You are early," he said.

"I am late," she answered. Already stepping out of her skirt.

I

Schoenmaker, being conservative, referred to his profession as the art of Tagliacozzi. His own methods, while not as primitive as those of the sixteenth-century Italian, were marked by a certain sentimental inertia, so that Schoenmaker was never quite up to date. He went out of his way to cultivate the Tagliacozzi look: showing his eyebrows thin and semicircular; wearing a bushy mustache, pointed beard, sometimes even a skullcap, his old schoolboy yarmulke.

He'd received his impetus—like the racket itself—from the World War. At seventeen, coeval with the century, he raised a mustache (which he never shaved off), falsified his age and name and wallowed off in a fetid troopship to fly, so he thought, high over the ruined châteaux and scarred fields of France, got up like an earless raccoon to scrimmage with the Hun; a brave Icarus.

Well, the kid never did get up in the air, but they made him a greasemonkey which was more than he'd expected anyway. It was enough. He got to know the guts not only of Breguets, Bristol Fighters and JN's, but also of the bird-men who did go up, and whom, of course, he adored. There was always a certain feudal-homosexual element in this division of labor. Schoenmaker felt like a page boy. Since those days as we know democracy has made its inroads and those crude flying-machines have evolved into "weapon systems" of a then undreamed-of complexity; so that the maintenance man today has to be as professional-noble as the flight crew he supports.

But then: it was a pure and abstract passion, directed for Schoenmaker, at least, toward the face. His own mustache may have been partly responsible; he was often mistaken for a pilot. On off hours, infrequently, he would sport a silk kerchief (obtained in Paris) at his throat, by way of imitation.

The war being what it was, certain of the faces—craggy or smooth, with slicked-down hair or bald—never came back. To this the young Schoenmaker responded with all adolescent love's flexibility: his free-floating affection sad and thwarted for a time till it managed to attach itself to a new face. But in each case, loss was as unspecified as the proposition "love dies." They flew off and were swallowed in the sky.

Until Evan Godolphin. A liaison officer in his middle thirties, TDY with the Americans for reconnaissance missions over the Argonne plateau, Godolphin carried the natural foppishness of the early aviators to extremes which in the time's hysterical context seemed perfectly normal. Here were no trenches, after all: the air up there was free of any taint of gas or comrades' decay. Combatants on both sides could afford to break champagne glasses in the majestic fireplaces of commandeered country seats; treat their captives with utmost courtesy, adhere to every point of the duello when it came to a dogfight; in short, practice with finicking care the entire rigmarole of nineteenth-century gentlemen at war. Evan Godolphin wore a Bond Street-tailored flying suit; would often, dashing clumsily across the scars of their makeshift airfield toward his French Spad, stop to pluck a lone poppy, survivor of strafing by autumn and the Germans (naturally aware of the Flanders Fields poem in Punch, three years ago when there'd still been an idealistic tinge to trench warfare), and insert it into one faultless lapel.

Godolphin became Schoenmaker's hero. Tokens tossed his way—an occasional salute, a "well done" for the preflights which came to be the boy-mechanic's responsibility, a tense smile—were hoarded fervently. Perhaps he saw an end also to this unrequited love; doesn't a latent sense of death always heighten the pleasure of such an "involvement"?

The end came soon enough. One rainy afternoon toward the end of the battle of Meuse-Argonne, Godolphin's crippled plane materialized suddenly out of all that gray, looped feebly, dipped on a wing toward the ground and slid like a kite in an air current toward the runway. It missed the runway by a hundred yards; by the time it impacted corpsmen and stretcher-bearers were already running out toward it. Schoenmaker happened to be nearby and tagged along, having no idea what had happened till he saw the heap of rags and splinters, already soggy in the rain, and from it, limping toward the medics, the worst possible travesty of a human face lolling atop an animate corpse. The top of the nose had been shot away; shrapnel had torn out part of one cheek and shattered half the chin. The eyes, intact, showed nothing.

Schoenmaker must have lost himself. The next he could remember he was back at an aid station, trying to convince the doctors there to take his own cartilage. Godolphin would live, they'd decided. But his face would have to be rebuilt. Life for the young officer would be, otherwise, unthinkable.

Now luckily for some a law of supply and demand had been at work in the field of plastic surgery. Godolphin's case, by 1918, was hardly unique. Methods had been in existence since the fifth century B.C. for rebuilding noses, Thiersch grafts had been around for forty or so years. During the war new techniques were developed by necessity and were practiced by GP's, eye-ear-nose-and-throat men, even a hastily recruited gynecologist or two. The techniques that worked were adopted and passed on quickly to the younger medics. Those that failed produced a generation of freaks and pariahs who along with those who'd received no restorative surgery at all became a secret and horrible postwar fraternity. No good at all in any of the usual rungs of society, where did they go?

(Profane would see some of them under the street. Others you could meet at any rural crossroads in America. As Profane had: come to a new road, right-angles to his progress, smelled the Diesel exhaust of a truck long gone—like walking through a ghost—and seen there like a milestone one of them. Whose limp might mean a brocade or bas-relief of scar tissue down one leg—how many women had looked and shied?—; whose cicatrix on the throat would be hidden modestly like a gaudy war decoration; whose tongue, protruding through a hole in the cheek, would never speak secret words with any extra mouth.)

Evan Godolphin proved to be one of them. The doctor was young, he had ideas of his own, which the AEF was no place for. His name was Halidom and he favored allografts: the introduction of inert substances into the living face. It was suspected at the time that the only safe transplants to use were cartilage or skin from the patient's own body. Schoenmaker, knowing nothing about medicine, offered his cartilage but the gift was rejected; allografting was plausible and Halidom saw no reason for two men being hospitalized when only one had to be.

Thus Godolphin received a nose bridge of ivory, a cheekbone of silver and a paraffin and celluloid chin. A month later Schoenmaker went to visit him in the hospital—the last time he ever saw Godolphin. The reconstruction had been perfect. He was being sent back to London, in some obscure staff position, and spoke with a grim flippancy.

"Take a long look. It won't be good for more than six months." Schoenmaker stammered: Godolphin continued: "See him, down the way?" Two cots over lay what would have been a similar casualty except that the skin of the face was whole, shiny. But the skull beneath was misshapen. "Foreign-body reaction, they call it. Sometimes infection, inflammation, sometimes only pain. The paraffin, for instance, doesn't hold shape. Before you know it, you're back where you started." He talked like a man under death sentence. "Perhaps I can pawn my cheekbone. It's worth a fortune. Before they

melted it down it was one of a set of pastoral figurines,
eighteenth century—nymphs, shepherdesses—looted from a
château the Hun was using for a CP; Lord knows where
they're originally from—"

"Couldn't—" Schoenmaker's throat was dry—"couldn't they
fix it, somehow: start over . . ."

"Too rushed. I'm lucky to get what I got. I can't complain.
Think of the devils who haven't even six months to bash
around in."

"What will you do when—"

"I'm not thinking of that. But it will be a grand six
months."

The young mechanic stayed in a kind of emotional limbo
for weeks. He worked without the usual slacking off, believing himself no more animate than the spanners and screw-
drivers he handled. When there were passes to be had he
gave his to someone else. He slept on an average of four
hours a night. This mineral period ended by an accidental
meeting with a medical officer one evening in the barracks.
Schoenmaker put it as primitively as he felt:

"How can I become a doctor?"

Of course it was idealistic and uncomplex. He wanted only
to do something for men like Godolphin, to help prevent a
takeover of the profession by its unnatural and traitorous
Halidoms. It took ten years of working at his first specialty—
mechanic—as well as navvy in a score of markets and ware-
houses, bill-collector, once administrative assistant to a boot-
legging syndicate operating out of Decatur, Illinois. These
years of labor were interlarded with night courses and occasional day enrollments, though none more than three se-
mesters in a row (after Decatur, when he could afford it);
internship; finally, on the eve of the Great Depression, entrance to the medical freemasonry.

If alignment with the inanimate is the mark of a Bad
Guy, Schoenmaker at least made a sympathetic beginning.
But at some point along his way there occurred a shift in
outlook so subtle that even Profane, who was unusually
sensitive that way, probably couldn't have detected it. He was
kept going by hatred for Halidom and perhaps a fading love
for Godolphin. These had given rise to what is called a "sense
of mission"—something so tenuous it has to be fed more
solid fare than either hatred or love. So it came to be sus-
tained, plausibly enough, by a number of bloodless the-

ories about the "idea" of the plastic surgeon. Having heard
his vocation on the embattled wind, Schoenmaker's dedica-
tion was toward repairing the havoc wrought by agencies
outside his own sphere of responsibility. Others—politicians
and machines—carried on wars; others—perhaps human
machines—condemned his patients to the ravages of acquired
syphilis; others—on the highways, in the factories—undid the
work of nature with automobiles, milling machines, other
instruments of civilian disfigurement. What could he do toward eliminating the causes? They existed, formed a body
of things-as-they-are; he came to be afflicted with a conservative laziness. It was social awareness of a sort, but with
boundaries and interfaces which made it less than the catholic rage filling him that night in the barracks with the M.O.
It was in short a deterioration of purpose; a decay.

II

Esther met him, oddly enough, through Stencil, who at the
time was only a newcomer to the Crew. Stencil, pursuing a
different trail, happened for reasons of his own to be interested in Evan Godolphin's history. He'd followed it as far as
Meuse-Argonne. Having finally got Schoenmaker's alias
from the AEF records, it took Stencil months to trace him
to Germantown and the Muzak-filled face hospital. The
good doctor denied everything, after every variety of cajole-
ment Stencil knew; it was another dead end.

As is usual after certain frustrations, we react with be-
nevolence. Esther had been languishing ripe and hot-eyed
about the Rusty Spoon, hating her figure-6 nose and proving
as well as she could the unhappy undergraduate adage: "All
the ugly ones fuck." The thwarted Stencil, casting about for
somebody to take it all out on, glommed on to her despair
hopefully—a taking which progressed to sad summer after-
noons wandering among parched fountains, sunstruck shop
fronts and streets bleeding tar, eventually to a father-daugh-
ter agreement casual enough to be canceled at any time
should either of them desire, no post-mortems necessary. It
struck him with a fine irony that the nicest sentimental
trinket for her would be an introduction to Schoenmaker;
accordingly, in September, the contact was made and Esther
without ado went under his knives and kneading fingers.

Collected for her in the anteroom that day were a rogues'

gallery of malformed. A bald woman without ears contemplated the gold imp-clock, skin flush and shiny from temples to occiput. Beside her sat a younger girl, whose skull was fissured such that three separate peaks, paraboloid in shape, protruded above the hair, which continued down either side of a densely acned face like a skipper's beard. Across the room, studying a copy of the Reader's Digest, sat an aged gentleman in a moss-green gabardine suit, who possessed three nostrils, no upper lip and an assortment of different-sized teeth which leaned and crowded together like the headstones of a boneyard in tornado country. And off in a corner, looking at nothing, was a sexless being with hereditary syphilis, whose bones had acquired lesions and had partially collapsed so that the gray face's profile was nearly a straight line, the nose hanging down like a loose flap of skin, nearly covering the mouth; the chin depressed at the side by a large sunken crater containing radial skin-wrinkles; the eyes squeezed shut by the same unnatural gravity that flattened the rest of the profile. Esther, who was still at an impressionable age, identified with them all. It was confirmation of this alien feeling which had driven her to bed with so many of the Whole Sick Crew.

This first day Schoenmaker spent in pre-operative reconnaissance of the terrain: photographing Esther's face and nose from various angles, checking for upper respiratory infections, running a Wassermann. Irving and Trench also assisted him in making two duplicate casts or death-masks. They gave her two paper straws to breathe through and in her childish way she thought of soda shops, cherry Cokes, True Confessions.

Next day she was back at the office. The two casts were there on his desk, side by side. "I'm twins," she giggled. Schoenmaker reached out and snapped the plaster nose from one of the masks.

"Now," he smiled; producing like a magician a lump of modeling clay with which he replaced the broken-off nose. "What sort of nose did you have in mind?"

What else: Irish, she wanted, turned up. Like they all wanted. To none of them did it occur that the retroussé nose too is an aesthetic misfit: a Jew nose in reverse, is all. Few had ever asked for a so-called "perfect" nose, where the roof is straight, the tip untilted and unhooked, the columella (separating the nostrils) meeting the upper lip at 90°. All

of which went to support his private thesis that correction
—along all dimensions: social, political, emotional—entails
retreat to a diametric opposite rather than any reasonable
search for a golden mean.

A few artistic finger-flourishes and wrist-twistings.
"Would that be it?" Eyes aglow, she nodded. "It has to
harmonize with the rest of your face, you see." It didn't, of
course. All that could harmonize with a face, if you were
going to be humanistic about it, was obviously what the face
was born with.

"But," he'd been able to rationalize years before, "there
is harmony and harmony." So, Esther's nose. Identical with
an ideal of nasal beauty established by movies, advertise-
ments, magazine illustrations. Cultural harmony, Schoenmaker called it.

"Try next week then." He gave her the time. Esther was
thrilled. It was like waiting to be born, and talking over
with God, calm and businesslike, exactly how you wanted to
enter the world.

Next week she arrived, punctual: guts tight, skin sensitive. "Come." Schoenmaker took her gently by the hand. She
felt passive, even (a little?) sexually aroused. She was seated
in a dentist's chair, tilted back and prepared by Irving, who
hovered about her like a handmaiden.

Esther's face was cleaned in the nasal region with green
soap, iodine and alcohol. The hair inside her nostrils was
clipped and the vestibules cleaned gently with antiseptics.
She was then given Nembutal.

It was expected this would calm her down, but barbituric
acid derivatives affect individuals differently. Perhaps her
initial sexual arousal contributed; but by the time Esther
was taken to the operating room she was near delirium.
"Should have used Hyoscin," Trench said. "It gives them
amnesia, man."

"Quiet, schlep," said the doctor, scrubbing. Irving set about
arranging his armamentarium, while Trench strapped Esther
to the operating table. Esther's eyes were wild; she sobbed
quietly, obviously beginning to get second thoughts. "Too late
now," Trench consoled her, grinning. "Lay quiet, hey."

All three wore surgical masks. The eyes looked suddenly
malevolent to Esther. She tossed her head. "Trench, hold her
head," came Schoenmaker's muffled voice, "and Irving can

be the anaesthetist. You need practice, babe. Go get the
Novocain bottle."

Sterile towels were placed under Esther's head and a
drop of castor oil in each eye. Her face was again swabbed,
this time with Metaphen and alcohol. Gauze packing was
then jammed far up her nostrils to keep antiseptics and
blood from flowing down her pharynx and throat.

Irving returned with the Novocain, a syringe, and a needle.
First she put the anaesthetic into the tip of Esther's nose,
one injection on each side. Next she made a number of injections radially around each nostril, to deaden the wings,
or alae, her thumb going down on the plunger each time
as the needle withdrew. "Switch to the big one," Schoenmaker
said quietly. Irving fished a two-inch needle out of the auto-
clave. This time the needle was pushed, just under the skin,
all the way up each side of the nose, from the nostril to where
the nose joined forehead.

No one had told Esther that anything about the operation
would hurt. But these injections hurt: nothing before in her
experience had ever hurt quite so much. All she had free
to move for the pain were her hips. Trench held her head
and leered appreciatively as she squirmed, constrained, on
the table.

Inside the nose again with another burden of anaesthetic,
Irving's hypodermic was inserted between the upper and
lower cartilage and pushed all the way up to the glabella—the
bump between the eyebrows.

A series of internal injections to the septum—the wall of
bone and cartilage which separates the two halves of the
nose—and anaesthesia was complete. The sexual metaphor
in all this wasn't lost on Trench, who kept chanting, "Stick
it in . . . pull it out . . . stick it in . . . ooh that was
good . . . pull it out . . ." and tittering softly above Esther's
eyes. Irving would sigh each time, exasperated. "That boy,"
you expected her to say.

After a while Schoenmaker started pinching and twisting
Esther's nose. "How does it feel? Hurt?" A whispered no:
Schoenmaker twisted harder: "Hurt?" No. "Okay. Cover her
eyes."

"Maybe she wants to look," Trench said.

"You want to look, Esther? See what we're going to do to
you?"

"I don't know." Her voice was weak, teetering between here and hysteria.

"Watch, then," said Schoenmaker. "Get an education. First we'll cut out the hump. Let's see a scalpel."

It was a routine operation; Schoenmaker worked quickly, neither he nor his nurse wasting any motion. Caressing sponge-strokes made it nearly bloodless. Occasionally a trickle would elude him and get halfway to the towels before he caught it.

Schoenmaker first made two incisions, one on either side through the internal lining of the nose, near the septum at the lower border of the side cartilage. He then pushed a pair of long-handled, curved and pointed scissors through the nostril, up past the cartilage to the nasal bone. The scissors had been designed to cut both on opening and closing. Quickly, like a barber finishing up a high-tipping head, he separated the bone from the membrane and skin over it. "Undermining, we call this," he explained. He repeated the scissors work through the other nostril. "You see you have two nasal bones, they're separated by your septum. At the bottom they're each attached to a piece of lateral cartilage. I'm undermining you all the way from this attachment to where the nasal bones join the forehead."

Irving passed him a chisel-like instrument. "MacKenty's elevator, this is." With the elevator he probed around, completing the undermining.

"Now," gently, like a lover, "I'm going to saw off your hump." Esther watched his eyes as best she could, looking for something human there. Never had she felt so helpless. Later she would say, "It was almost a mystic experience. What religion is it—one of the Eastern ones—where the highest condition we can attain is that of an object—a rock. It was like that; I felt myself drifting down, this delicious loss of Estherhood, becoming more and more a blob, with no worries, traumas, nothing: only Being. . . ."

The mask with the clay nose lay on a small table nearby. Referring to it with quick side-glances, Schoenmaker inserted the saw blade through one of the incisions he'd made, and pushed it up to the bony part. Then lined it up with the line of the new nose-roof and carefully began to saw through the nasal bone on that side. "Bone saws easily," he remarked to Esther. "We're all really quite frail." The blade reached

soft septum; Schoenmaker withdrew the blade. "Now comes
the tricky part. I got to saw off the other side exactly the
same. Otherwise your nose will be lopsided." He inserted
the saw in the same way on the other side, studied the
mask for what seemed to Esther a quarter of an hour; made
several minute adjustments. Then finally sawed off the bone
there in a straight line.

"Your hump is now two loose pieces of bone, attached
only to the septum. We have to cut that through, flush
with the other two cuts." This he did with an angle-bladed
pull-knife, cutting down swiftly, completing the phase with
some graceful sponge-flourishing.

"And now the hump floats inside the nose." He pulled
back one nostril with a retractor, inserted a pair of forceps
and fished around for the hump. "Take that back," he
smiled. "It doesn't want to come just yet." With scissors he
snipped the hump loose from the lateral cartilage which had
been holding it; then, with the bone-forceps, removed a dark-
colored lump of gristle, which he waved triumphantly before Esther. "Twenty-two years of social unhappiness, nicht
wahr? End of act one. We'll put it in formaldehyde, you
can keep it for a souvenir if you wish." As he talked he
smoothed the edges of the cuts with a small rasp file.

So much for the hump. But where the hump had been
was now a flat area. The bridge of the nose had been too
wide to begin with, and now had to be narrowed.

Again he undermined the nasal bones, this time around
to where they met the cheekbones, and beyond. As he removed the scissors he inserted a right-angled saw in its
place. "Your nasal bones are anchored firmly, you see; at
the side to the cheekbone, at the top to the forehead. We
must fracture them, so we can move your nose around.
Just like that lump of clay."

He sawed through the nasal bones on each side, separating them from the cheekbones. He then took a chisel
and inserted it through one nostril, pushing it as high as
he could, until it touched bone.

"Let me know if you feel anything." He gave the chisel
a few light taps with a mallet; stopped, puzzled, and then
began to hammer harder. "It's a rough mother," he said,
dropping his jocular tone. Tap, tap, tap. "Come on, you
bastard." The chisel point edged its way, millimeter by milli-

meter, between Esther's eyebrows. "Scheisse!" With a loud snap, her nose was broken free of the forehead. By pushing in from either side with his thumbs, Schoenmaker completed the fracture.

"See? It's all wobbly now. That's act two. Now ve shorten das septum, ja."

With a scalpel he made an incision around the septum, between it and its two adjoining lateral cartilages. He then cut down around the front of the septum to the "spine," located just inside the nostrils at the back.

"Which should give you a free-floating septum. We use scissors to finish the job." With dissecting scissors he undermined the septum along its sides and up over the bones as far as the glabella, at the top of the nose.

He passed a scalpel next into one of the incisions just inside the nostril and out the other, and worked the cutting edge around until the septum was separated at the bottom. Then elevated one nostril with a retractor, reached in with Allis clamps and pulled out part of the loose septum. A quick transfer of calipers from mask to exposed septum; then with a pair of straight scissors Schoenmaker snipped off a triangular wedge of septum. "Now to put everything in place."

Keeping one eye on the mask, he brought together the nasal bones. This narrowed the bridge and eliminated the flat part where the hump had been cut off. He took some time making sure the two halves were lined up dead-center. The bones made a curious crackling sound as he moved them. "For your turned-up nose, we make two sutures."

The "seam" was between the recently-cut edge of the septum and the columella. With needle and needle-holder, two silk stitches were taken obliquely, through the entire widths of columella and septum.

The operation had taken, in all, less than an hour. They cleaned Esther up, removed the plain gauze packing and replaced it with sulfa ointment and more gauze. A strip of adhesive tape went on over her nostrils, another over the bridge of the new nose. On top of this went a Stent mold, a tin guard, and more adhesive plaster. Rubber tubes were put in each nostril so she could breathe.

Two days later the packing was removed. The adhesive

plaster came off after five days. The sutures came out after
seven. The uptilted end product looked ridiculous but Schoenmaker assured her it would come down a little after a few
months. It did.

III

That would have been all: except for Esther. Possibly her
old humpnosed habits had continued on by virtue of mo-
mentum. But never before had she been so passive with any
male. Passivity having only one meaning for her, she left
the hospital Schoenmaker had sent her to after a day and a
night, and roamed the East Side in fugue, scaring people
with her white beak and a certain shock about the eyes.
She was sexually turned on, was all: as if Schoenmaker had
located and flipped a secret switch or clitoris somewhere
inside her nasal cavity. A cavity is a cavity, after all: Trench's
gift for metaphor might have been contagious.

Returning the following week to have the stitches removed,
she crossed and uncrossed her legs, batted eyelashes, talked
soft: everything crude she knew. Schoenmaker had spotted
her at the outset as an easy make.

"Come back tomorrow," he told her. Irving was off.
Esther arrived the next day garbed underneath as lacily and
with as many fetishes as she could afford. There might even
have been a dab of Shalimar on the gauze in the center of
her face.

In the back room: "How do you feel?"

She laughed, too loud. "It hurts. But."

"Yes, but. There are ways to forget the pain."

She seemed unable to get rid of a silly, half-apologetic
smile. It stretched her face, adding to the pain in her nose.

"Do you know what we're going to do? No, what I am
going to do to you? Of course."

She let him undress her. He commented only on a black
garter belt.

"Oh. Oh God." An attack of conscience: Slab had given
it to her. With love, presumably.

"Stop. Stop the peep-show routine. You're not a virgin."

Another self-deprecating laugh. "That's just it. Another
boy. Gave it to me. Boy that I loved."

She's in shock, he thought, vaguely surprised.

"Come. We'll make believe it's your operation. You enjoyed your operation, didn't you."

Through a crack in the curtains opposite Trench looked on.

"Lie on the bed. That will be our operating table. You are to get an intermuscular injection."

"No," she cried.

"You have worked on many ways of saying no. No meaning yes. That no I don't like. Say it differently."

"No," with a little moan.

"Different. Again."

"No," this time a smile, eyelids at half-mast.

"Again."

"No."

"You're getting better." Unknotting his tie, trousers in a puddle about his feet, Schoenmaker serenaded her.

> Have I told you, fella
> She's got the sweetest columella
> And a septum that's swept 'em all on their ass;
> Each casual chondrectomy
> Meant only a big fat check to me
> Till I sawed this osteoclastible lass:

[Refrain]:

> Till you've cut into Esther
> You've cut nothing at all;
> She's one of the best, Thir,
> To her nose I'm in thrall.

> She never acts nasty
> But lies still as a rock;
> She loves my rhinoplasty
> But the others are schlock.

> Esther is passive,
> Her aplomb is massive,
> How could any poor ass've
> Ever passed her by?

And let me to you say
She puts Ireland to shame;
For her nose is retroussé
And Esther's her name. . . .

For the last eight bars she chanted "No" on one and three.
    Such was the (as it were) Jacobean etiology of Esther's
eventual trip to Cuba; which see.

BRUCE JAY FRIEDMAN

Black Angels

Smothered by debt, his wife and child in flight, Stefano held fast to his old house in the country, a life buoy in a sea of despair. Let him but keep up the house, return to it each day; before long, his wife would come to her senses, fly back to him. Yet he dreaded the approach of spring, which meant large teams of gardeners who would charge him killing prices to keep the place in shape. Cheapest of all had been the Angeluzzi Brothers who had gotten him off the ground with a two-hundred-and-fifty-dollar cleanup, then followed through with ninety dollars a month for maintenance, April through October, a hundred extra for the leaf-raking fall windup. Meticulous in April, the four Angeluzzis soon began to dog it; for his ninety, Stefano got only a few brisk lawn cuts and a swipe or two at his flower beds. This spring, unable to work, his life in shreds, Stefano held off on the grounds as long as he could. The grass grew to his shins until one day Swansdowne, a next-door neighbor who had won marigold contests, called on another subject, but with much lawn-mowing and fertilizing in his voice. Stefano dialed the Angeluzzis; then, on an impulse, he dropped the phone and reached for the local paper, running his finger along Home Services. A gardener named Please Try Us caught his fancy. He called the number, asked the deep voice at the other end to come by soon and give him an estimate. The following night, a return call came through.

"I have seen and checked out the place," said the voice, the tones heavy, resonant, solid.

"What'll you take for cleanup?" asked Stefano. "We'll start there."

Long pause. Lip smack. Then, "Thutty dollars."

"Which address did you go to? I'm at 42 Spring. Big old place on the corner of Spring and Rooter."

"That's correct. For fertilizing, that'll be eight extra, making thutty-eight."

"Awful lot of work here," said Stefano, confused, tingling with both guilt and relief. "All right, when can you get at it?"

"Tomorrow morning. Eight o'clock."

"You're on."

Stefano watched them arrive the next day, Sunday, a quartet of massive Negroes in two trucks and two sleek private cars. In stifling heat, they worked in checkered shirts and heavy pants, two with fedoras impossibly balanced on the backs of their great shaved heads. Stefano, a free-lance writer of technical manuals, went back to his work, stopping now and then to check the Negroes through the window. How could they possibly make out on thirty-eight dollars, he wondered. Divided four ways it came to nothing. Gas alone for their fleet of cars would kill their nine-fifty each. He'd give them forty-five dollars to salve his conscience, but still, what about their groceries, rent? Late in the afternoon, he ran out with beers for each. "Plenty of leaves, eh?" he said to Cotten, largest of them, the leader, expressionless in dainty steel-rimmed glasses.

"Take about two and a half days," said the Negro.

"I'm giving you forty-five dollars," said Stefano. "What the hell."

The job actually took three full days, two for the cleanup, a third for the lawn and fertilizing the beds. The last day was a bad one for Stefano. Through his window, he watched the black giants trim the lawn, then kneel in winter clothes and lovingly collect what seemed to be each blade of grass so there'd be no mess. He wanted to run out and tell them to do less work; certainly not at those prices. Yet he loved the prices, too. He could take it all out of expense money, not even bother his regular free-lance payments. At the end of the day, he walked up to Cotten, took out his wallet and said, "I'm giving you cash. So you won't have to bother with a check." It had occurred to him that perhaps the Negroes only did cleanups, no maintenance. By doing enough of them, thousands, perhaps they could sneak by, somehow make a living. "What about maintenance?" he asked the head gardener.

The man scratched his ear, shook his head, finally said, "Can't do your place for less than eighteen dollars a month."

"You guys do some work," said Stefano, shivering with glee. "Best I've seen. I think you're too low. I'll give you twenty-two."

The Negroes came back twice a week, turned Stefano's home into a showplace, hacking down dead trees, planting new ones, filling in dead spots, keeping the earth black and loamy. Swansdowne, who usually let Stefano test-run new gardeners and then swooped down to sign them up if they were good, looked on with envy, yet called one day and said, "I would never let a colored guy touch my place."

"They're doing a great job on mine," said Stefano.

Maybe that explains it, he thought. All of the Swans-downes who won't have Negro gardeners. That's why their rates are low. Otherwise, they'd starve. He felt good, a liberal. Why shouldn't he get a slight break on money?

At the end of May, Stefano paid them their twenty-two dollars and distributed four American-cheese sandwiches. The three assistants took them back to a truck where one had mayonnaise. "You guys do other kinds of work?" Stefano asked Cotten, who leaned on a hoe. "What about painting? A house?"

The gardener looked up at Stefano's colonial. "We do," he said.

"How much would you take?" The best estimate on the massive ten-roomer had been seven hundred dollars.

"Fifty-eight dollars," said the huge Negro, neutral in his steel-rims.

"I'll pay for half the paint," said Stefano.

The following day, when Stefano awakened, the four Negroes, on high, buckling ladders, had half the house done, the paint deep brown, rich and gurgling in the sun. Their gardening clothes were spattered with paint. He'd pick up the cleaning bill, thought Stefano. It was only fair.

"It looks great!" he hollered up to Cotten, swaying mas-sively in the wind.

"She'll shape up time we get the fourth coat on."

By mid-June, the four Negroes had cleaned out Stefano's attic for three dollars, waterproofed his basement for an-other sixteen; an elaborate network of drainage pipes went in for twelve-fifty. One day he came home to find the floors cleaned, sanded, shellacked, his cabinets scrubbed, linen closets dizzying in their cleanliness. Irritated for the first time—I didn't order this—he melted quickly when he saw the bill. A slip on the bread box read: "You owes us $2.80." Loving the breaks he was getting, Stefano threw them bonuses, plenty of sandwiches, all his old sports jackets, venetian blinds that had come out of the attic and books of fairly recent vintage on Nova Scotia tourism. Never in the thick of marriage had his place been so immaculate; cars slowed down to admire his dramatically painted home, his shrubs bursting with fertility. Enter any room; its cleanliness would tear your head off. With all these ridiculously cheap home services going for him, Stefano felt at times his luck had turned. Still, a cloak of loneliness rode his shoulders, aggravation clogged his throat. If only to hate her, he missed his wife, a young, pretty woman, circling the globe with her lover, an assistant director on daytime TV. He saw pictures of her, tumbling with lust, in staterooms, inns, the backs of small foreign cars. He missed his son, too, a boy of ten, needing braces. God only knows what shockers he was being exposed to. The pair had fled in haste, leaving behind mementos, toys lined up on shelves, dresses spilling out of chests. Aging quickly, his confidence riddled, Stefano failed in his quest for dates with young girls, speechless and uncertain on the phone. What could he do with himself. At these prices, he could keep his home spotless. But would that make everything all right. Would that haul back a disgruntled wife and son. One night, his heart weighing a ton, he returned from an "Over 28" dance to find the burly Negroes winding up their work. Sweating long into the night, they had rigged up an elaborate network of gas lamps, the better to show off a brilliantly laid out thicket of tea roses and dwarf fruit trees. Total cost for the lighting: Five dollars and fifty cents.

"Really lovely," said Stefano, inspecting his grounds, counting out some bills. "Here," he said to the head gardener. "Take another deuce. In my condition, money means nothing." The huge Negro toweled down his forehead, gathered up his equipment. "Hey," said Stefano. "Come on in for a beer. If I don't talk to someone I'll bust."

"Got to get on," said Cotten. "We got work to do."

"Come on, come on," said Stefano. "What can you do at this hour. Give a guy a break."

The Negro shook his head in doubt, then moved massively toward the house, Stefano clapping him on the back in a show of brotherhood.

Inside, Stefano went for flip-top beers. The gardener sat down in the living room, his great bulk caving deeply into the sofa. For a moment, Stefano worried about gardening clothes, Negro ones to boot, in contact with living-room furniture, then figured the hell with it, who'd complain.

"I've got the worst kind of trouble," said Stefano, leaning back on a Danish modern slat bench. "Sometimes I don't think I'm going to make it through the night. My wife's checked out on me. You probably figured that out already."

The Negro crossed his great legs, sipped his beer. The steel-rimmed glasses had a shimmer to them and Stefano could not make out his eyes.

"She took the kid with her," said Stefano. "That may be the worst part. You don't know what it's like to have a kid tearing around your house for ten years and then not to hear anything. Or maybe you do?" Stefano asked hopefully. "You probably have a lot of trouble of your own."

Silent, the Negro sat forward and shoved a cloth inside his flannel shirt to mop his chest.

"Anyway, I'll be goddamned if I know what to do. Wait around? Pretend she's never coming back? I don't know what in the hell to do with myself. Where do I go from here?"

"How long she gone?" asked the guest, working on the back of his neck now.

"What's that got to do with it?" asked Stefano. "About four months, I guess. Just before you guys came. Oh, I see what you mean. If she hasn't come back in four months, she's probably gone for good. I might as well start building a new life. That's a good point."

The Negro put away the cloth and folded his legs again, crossing his heavy, blunted fingers, arranging them on the point of one knee.

"It just happened out of the clear blue sky," said Stefano. "Oh, why kid around. It was never any good." He told the Negro about their courtship, the false pregnancy, how he had been "forced" to get married. Then he really started in on his wife, the constant primping, the thousands of ways she had made him jealous, the in-laws to support. He let it all come out of him, like air from a tire, talking with heat and fury; until he realized he had been talking non-stop for maybe twenty minutes, half an hour. The Negro listened to him, patiently, not bothering with his beer. Finally, when Stefano sank back to catch his breath, the gardener asked a question: "You think you any good?"

"What do you mean," said Stefano. "Of course I do. Oh, I get what you're driving at. If I thought I was worth anything, I wouldn't let all of this kill me. I'd just kind of brace myself, dig out and really build something fine for myself. Funny how you make just the right remark. It's really amazing. You know I've done the analysis bit. Never meant a damned thing to me. I've had nice analysts, tough ones, all kinds. But the way you just let me sound off and then asked that one thing. This is going to sound crazy, but what if we just talked this way, couple of times a week. I just sound off and then you come in with the haymaker, the way you just did. Just for fun, what would you charge me? An hour?"

"Fo' hundred," said the Negro.

"Four hundred. That's really a laugh. You must be out of your head. What are you, crazy? Don't you know I was just kidding around."

The Negro took a sip of the beer and rose to leave. "All right, wait a second," said Stefano. "Hold on a minute. Let's just finish up this hour, all right. Then we'll see about other times. This one doesn't count, does it?"

"It do," said the Negro, sinking into the couch and producing pad and pencil.

"That's not really fair, you know," said Stefano. "To count this one. Anyway, we'll see. Maybe we'll try it for awhile. That's some price. Where was I? Whew, all that money. To get back to what I was saying, this girl has been a bitch ever since the day I laid eyes on her. You made me see it tonight. In many ways, I think she's a lot like my mom. . . ."

JOSEPH HELLER

Milo

April had been the best month of all for Milo. Lilacs bloomed in April and fruit ripened on the vine. Heartbeats quickened and old appetites were renewed. In April a livelier iris gleamed upon the burnished dove. April was spring, and in the spring Milo Minderbinder's fancy had lightly turned to thoughts of tangerines.

"Tangerines?"

"Yes, sir."

"My men would love tangerines," admitted the colonel in Sardinia who commanded four squadrons of B-25s.

"There'll be all the tangerines they can eat that you're able to pay for with money from your mess fund," Milo assured him.

"Casaba melons?"

"Are going for a song in Damascus."

"I have a weakness for casaba melons. I've always had a weakness for casaba melons."

"Just lend me one plane from each squadron, just one plane, and you'll have all the casabas you can eat that you've money to pay for."

"We buy from the syndicate?"

"And everybody has a share."

"It's amazing, positively amazing. How can you do it?"

"Mass purchasing power makes the big difference. For example, breaded veal cutlets."

"I'm not so crazy about breaded veal cutlets," grumbled

the skeptical B-25 commander in the north of Corsica.

"Breaded veal cutlets are very nutritious," Milo admonished him piously. "They contain egg yolk and bread crumbs. And so are lamb chops."

"Ah, lamb chops," echoed the B-25 commander. "Good lamb chops?"

"The best," said Milo, "that the black market has to offer."

"Baby lamb chops?"

"In the cutest little pink paper panties you ever saw. Are going for a song in Portugal."

"I can't send a plane to Portugal. I haven't the authority."

"I can, once you lend the plane to me. With a pilot to fly it. And don't forget—you'll get General Dreedle."

"Will General Dreedle eat in my mess hall again?"

"Like a pig, once you start feeding him my best white fresh eggs fried in my pure creamery butter. There'll be tangerines too, and casaba melons, honeydews, filet of Dover sole, baked Alaska, and cockles and mussels."

"And everybody has a share?"

"That," said Milo, "is the most beautiful part of it."

"I don't like it," growled the uncooperative fighter-plane commander, who didn't like Milo either.

"There's an uncooperative fighter-plane commander up north who's got it in for me," Milo complained to General Dreedle. "It takes just one person to ruin the whole thing, and then you wouldn't have your fresh eggs fried in my pure creamery butter any more."

General Dreedle had the uncooperative fighter-plane commander transferred to the Solomon Islands to dig graves and replaced him with a senile colonel with bursitis and a craving for litchi nuts who introduced Milo to the B-17 general on the mainland with a yearning for Polish sausage.

"Polish sausage is going for peanuts in Cracow," Milo informed him.

"Polish sausage," sighed the general nostalgically. "You know, I'd give just about anything for a good hunk of Polish sausage. Just about anything."

"You don't have to give *anything*. Just give me one plane for each mess hall and a pilot who will do what he's told. And a small down payment on your initial order as a token of good faith."

"But Cracow is hundreds of miles behind the enemy lines. How will you get to the sausage?"

"There's an international Polish sausage exchange in Geneva. I'll just fly the peanuts into Switzerland and exchange them for Polish sausage at the open market rate. They'll fly the peanuts back to Cracow and I'll fly the Polish sausage back to you. You buy only as much Polish sausage as you want through the syndicate. There'll be tangerines too, with only a little artificial coloring added. And eggs from Malta and Scotch from Sicily. You'll be paying the money to yourself when you buy from the syndicate, since you'll own a share, so you'll really be getting everything you buy for nothing. Doesn't that make sense?"

"Sheer genius. How in the world did you ever think of it?"

"My name is Milo Minderbinder. I am twenty-seven years old."

Milo Minderbinder's planes flew in from everywhere, the pursuit planes, bombers, and cargo ships streaming into Colonel Cathcart's field with pilots at the controls who would do what they were told. The planes were decorated with flamboyant squadron emblems illustrating such laudable ideals as Courage, Might, Justice, Truth, Liberty, Love, Honor and Patriotism that were painted out at once by Milo's mechanics with a double coat of flat white and replaced in garish purple with the stenciled name M & M ENTERPRISES, FINE FRUITS AND PRODUCE. The "M & M" in "M & M ENTERPRISES" stood for Milo & Minderbinder, and the & was inserted, Milo revealed candidly, to nullify any impression that the syndicate was a one-man operation. Planes arrived for Milo from airfields in Italy, North Africa and England, and from Air Transport Command stations in Liberia, Ascension Island, Cairo and Karachi. Pursuit planes were traded for additional cargo ships or retained for emergency invoice duty and small-parcel service; trucks and tanks were procured from the ground forces and used for short-distance road hauling. Everybody had a share, and men got fat and moved about tamely with toothpicks in their greasy lips. Milo supervised the whole expanding operation by himself. Deep otter-brown lines of preoccupation etched themselves permanently into his careworn face and gave him a harried look of sobriety and mistrust. Everybody but Yossarian thought Milo was a jerk, first for volunteering for the job of mess officer and next for taking it so seriously. Yossarian also thought that Milo was a jerk; but he also knew that Milo was a genius.

One day Milo flew away to England to pick up a load of Turkish halvah and came flying back from Madagascar leading four German bombers filled with yams, collards, mustard greens and black-eyed Georgia peas. Milo was dumfounded when he stepped down to the ground and found a contingent of armed M.P.s waiting to imprison the German pilots and confiscate their planes. *Confiscate!* The mere word was anathema to him, and he stormed back and forth in excoriating condemnation, shaking a piercing finger of rebuke in the guilt-ridden faces of Colonel Cathcart, Colonel Korn and the poor battle-scarred captain with the submachine gun who commanded the M.P.s.

"Is this Russia?" Milo assailed them incredulously at the top of his voice. *"Confiscate?"* he shrieked, as though he could not believe his own ears. "Since when is it the policy of the American government to confiscate the private property of its citizens? Shame on you! Shame on all of you for even thinking such a horrible thought."

"But Milo," Major Danby interrupted timidly, "we're at war with Germany, and those are German planes."

"They are no such thing!" Milo retorted furiously. "Those planes belong to the syndicate, and everybody has a share. *Confiscate?* How can you possibly confiscate your own private property? *Confiscate,* indeed! I've never heard anything so depraved in my whole life."

And sure enough, Milo was right, for when they looked, his mechanics had painted out the German swastikas on the wings, tails and fuselages with double coats of flat white and stenciled in the words M & M ENTERPRISES, FINE FRUITS AND PRODUCE. Right before their eyes he had transformed his syndicate into an international cartel.

Milo's argosies of plenty now filled the air. Planes poured in from Norway, Denmark, France, Germany, Austria, Italy, Yugoslavia, Romania, Bulgaria, Sweden, Finland, Poland—from everywhere in Europe, in fact, but Russia, with whom Milo refused to do business. When everybody who was going to had signed up with M & M Enterprises, Fine Fruits and Produce, Milo created a wholly owned subsidiary, M & M Enterprises, Fancy Pastry, and obtained more airplanes and more money from the mess funds for scones and crumpets from the British Isles, prune and cheese Danish from Copenhagen, éclairs, cream puffs, Napoleons and *petits fours* from Paris, Reims and Grenoble, *Kugelhopf*, pumpernickel and *Pfefferkuchen* from Berlin, *Linzer* and *Dobos Torten* from Vienna, *Strudel* from Hungary and *baklava* from Ankara. Each morning Milo sent planes aloft all over Europe and North Africa hauling long red tow signs advertising the day's specials in large square letters: "EYE ROUND, 79¢ . . . WHITING, 21¢." He boosted cash income for the syndicate by leasing tow signs to Pet Milk, Gaines Dog Food, and Noxzema. In a spirit of civic enterprise, he regularly allotted a certain amount of free aerial advertising space to General Peckem for the propagation of such messages in the public interest as NEATNESS COUNTS, HASTE MAKES WASTE, and THE FAMILY THAT PRAYS TOGETHER STAYS TOGETHER. Milo purchased spot radio announcements on Axis Sally's and Lord Haw Haw's daily propaganda broadcasts from Berlin to keep things moving. Business boomed on every battlefront.

Milo's planes were a familiar sight. They had freedom of passage everywhere, and one day Milo contracted with the American military authorities to bomb the German-held highway bridge at Orvieto and with the German military authorities to defend the highway bridge at Orvieto with antiaircraft fire against his own attack. His fee for attacking the bridge for America was the total cost of the operation plus six per cent, and his fee from Germany for defending the bridge was the same cost-plus-six agreement augmented by a merit bonus of a thousand dollars for every American plane he shot down. The consummation of these deals represented an important victory for private enterprise, he pointed out, since the armies of both countries were socialized institutions. Once the contracts were signed, there seemed to be no point in using the resources of the syndicate to bomb and defend the bridge, inasmuch as both governments had ample men and material right there to do so and were perfectly happy to contribute them, and in the end Milo realized a fantastic profit from both halves of his project for doing nothing more than signing his name twice.

The arrangements were fair to both sides. Since Milo did have freedom of passage everywhere, his planes were able to steal over in a sneak attack without alerting the German antiaircraft gunners; and since Milo knew about the attack, he was able to alert the German antiaircraft gunners in sufficient time for them to begin firing accurately the moment the planes came into range. It was an ideal arrangement for everyone but the dead man in Yossarian's tent, who was killed over the target the day he arrived.

"I didn't kill him!" Milo kept replying passionately to Yossarian's angry protest. "I wasn't even there that day, I tell you. Do you think I was down there on the ground firing an antiaircraft gun when the planes came over?"

"But you organized the whole thing, didn't you?" Yossarian shouted back at him in the velvet darkness cloaking the path leading past the still vehicles of the motor pool to the open-air movie theater.

"And I didn't organize anything," Milo answered indignantly, drawing great agitated sniffs of air in through his hissing, pale, twitching nose. "The Germans have the bridge, and we were going to bomb it, whether I stepped into the picture or not. I just saw a wonderful opportunity to make some profit out of the mission, and I took it. What's so terrible about that?"

"What's so terrible about it? Milo, a man in my tent was killed on that mission before he could even unpack his bags."

"But I didn't kill him."

"You got a thousand dollars extra for it."

"But I didn't kill him. I wasn't even there, I tell you. I was in Barcelona buying olive oil and skinless and boneless sardines, and I've got the purchase orders to prove it. And I didn't get the thousand dollars. That thousand dollars went to the syndicate, and everybody got a share, even you." Milo was appealing to Yossarian from the bottom of his soul. "Look, I didn't start this war, Yossarian, no matter what that lousy Wintergreen is saying. I'm just trying to put it on a businesslike basis. Is anything wrong with that? You know, a thousand dollars ain't such a bad price for a medium bomber and a crew. If I can persuade the Germans to pay me a thousand dollars for every plane they shoot down, why shouldn't I take it?"

"Because you're dealing with the enemy, that's why. Can't you understand that we're fighting a war? People are dying. Look around you, for Christ's sake!"

Milo shook his head with weary forbearance. "And the

Germans are not our enemies," he declared. "Oh, I know what you're going to say. Sure, we're at war with them. But the Germans are also members in good standing of the syndicate, and it's my job to protect their rights as shareholders. Maybe they did start the war, and maybe they are killing millions of people, but they pay their bills a lot more promptly than some allies of ours I could name. Don't you understand that I have to respect the sanctity of my contract with Germany? Can't you see it from my point of view?"

"No," Yossarian rebuffed him harshly.

Milo was stung and made no effort to disguise his wounded feelings. It was a muggy, moonlit night filled with gnats, moths, and mosquitoes. Milo lifted his arm suddenly and pointed toward the open-air theater, where the milky, dust-filled beam bursting horizontally from the projector slashed a conelike swath in the blackness and draped in a fluorescent membrane of light the audience tilted on the seats there in hypnotic sags, their faces focused upward toward the aluminized movie screen. Milo's eyes were liquid with integrity, and his artless and uncorrupted face was lustrous with a shining mixture of sweat and insect repellent.

"Look at them," he exclaimed in a voice choked with emotion. "They're my friends, my countrymen, my comrades in arms. A fellow never had a better bunch of buddies. Do you think I'd do a single thing to harm them if I didn't have to? Haven't I got enough on my mind? Can't you see how upset I am already about all that cotton piling up on those piers in Egypt?" Milo's voice splintered into fragments, and he clutched at Yossarian's shirt front as though drowning. His eyes were throbbing visibly like brown caterpillars. "Yossarian, what am I going to do with so much cotton? It's all your fault for letting me buy it."

The cotton was piling up on the piers in Egypt, and nobody wanted any. Milo had never dreamed that the Nile Valley could be so fertile or that there would be no market at all for the crop he had bought. The mess halls in his syndicate would not help; they rose up in uncompromising rebellion against his proposal to tax them on a per capita basis in order to enable each man to own his own share of the Egyptian cotton crop. Even his reliable friends the Germans failed him in this crisis: they preferred ersatz. Milo's mess halls would not even help him store the cotton, and his warehousing costs skyrocketed and contributed to the devastating drain upon his cash reserves. The profits from the Orvieto mission were sucked away. He began writing home for the money he had sent back in better days; soon that was almost gone. And new bales of cotton kept arriving on the wharves at Alexandria every day. Each time he succeeded in dumping some on the world market for a loss it was snapped up by canny Egyptian brokers in the Levant, who sold it back to him at the original contract price, so that he was really worse off than before.

M & M Enterprises verged on collapse. Milo cursed himself hourly for his monumental greed and stupidity in purchasing the entire Egyptian cotton crop, but a contract was a contract and had to be honored, and one night, after a sumptuous evening meal, all Milo's fighters and bombers took off, joined in formation directly overhead and began dropping bombs on the group. He had landed another contract with the Germans, this time to bomb his own outfit. Milo's planes separated in a well-co-ordinated attack and bombed the fuel stocks and the ordnance dump, the repair hangars and the B-25 bombers resting on the lollipop-shaped hardstands at the field. His crews spared the landing strip and the mess halls so that they could land safely when their work was done and enjoy a hot snack before retiring. They bombed with their landing lights on, since no one was shooting back. They bombed all four squadrons, the officers' club and the Group Headquarters building. Men bolted from their tents in sheer terror and did not know in which direction to turn. Wounded soon lay screaming everywhere. A cluster of fragmentation bombs exploded in the yard of the officers' club and punched jagged holes in the side of the wooden building and in the bellies and backs of a row of lieutenants and captains standing at the bar. They doubled over in agony and dropped. The rest of the officers fled toward the two exits in panic and jammed up the doorways like a dense, howling dam of human flesh as they shrank from going farther.

Colonel Cathcart clawed and elbowed his way through the unruly, bewildered mass until he stood outside by himself. He stared up at the sky in stark astonishment and horror. Milo's planes, ballooning serenely in over the blossoming treetops with their bomb bay doors open and wing flaps down and with their monstrous, bug-eyed, blinding, fiercely flickering, eerie landing lights on, were the most apocalyptic sight he had ever beheld. Colonel Cathcart let go a stricken gasp of dismay and hurled himself headlong into his jeep, almost sobbing. He found the gas pedal and the ignition and sped toward the airfield as fast as the rocking car would carry him, his huge flabby hands clenched and bloodless on the wheel or blaring his horn tormentedly. Once he almost killed himself when he swerved with a banshee screech of tires to avoid plowing into a bunch of men running crazily toward the hills in their underwear with their stunned faces down and their thin arms pressed high around their temples as puny shields. Yellow, orange and red fires were burning on both sides of the road. Tents and trees were in flames, and Milo's planes kept coming around interminably with their blinking white landing lights on and their bomb bay doors open. Colonel Cathcart almost turned the jeep over when he slammed the brakes on at the control tower. He leaped from the car while it was still skidding dangerously and hurtled up the flight of steps inside, where three men were busy at the instruments and the controls. He bowled two of them aside in his lunge for the nickel-plated microphone, his eyes glittering wildly and his beefy face contorted with stress. He squeezed the microphone in a bestial grip and began shouting hysterically at the top of his voice,

"Milo, you son of a bitch! Are you crazy? What the hell are you doing? Come down! Come down!"

"Stop hollering so much, will you?" answered Milo, who was standing there right beside him in the control tower with a microphone of his own. "I'm right here." Milo looked at him with reproof and turned back to his work. "Very good, men, very good," he chanted into his microphone. "But I see one supply shed still standing. That will never do, Purvis—I've spoken to you about that kind of shoddy work before. Now, you go right back there this minute and try it again. And this time come in slowly . . . slowly. Haste makes waste, Purvis. Haste makes waste. If I've told you that once, I must have told you that a hundred times. Haste makes waste."

The loud-speaker overhead began squawking. "Milo, this is Alvin Brown. I've finished dropping my bombs. What should I do now?"

"Strafe," said Milo.

"*Strafe?*" Alvin Brown was shocked.

"We have no choice," Milo informed him resignedly. "It's in the contract."

"Oh, okay, then," Alvin Brown acquiesced. "In that case I'll strafe."

This time Milo had gone too far. Bombing his own men and planes was more than even the most phlegmatic observer could stomach, and it looked like the end for him. High-ranking government officials poured in to investigate. Newspapers inveighed against Milo with glaring headlines, and Congressmen denounced the atrocity in stentorian wrath and clamored for punishment. Mothers with children in the service organized into militant groups and demanded revenge. Not one voice was raised in his defense. Decent people everywhere were affronted, and Milo was all washed up until he opened his books to the public and disclosed the tremendous profit he had made. He could reimburse the government for all the people and property he had destroyed and still have enough money left over to continue buying Egyptian cotton. Everybody, of course, owned a share. And the sweetest part of the whole deal was that there really was no need to reimburse the government at all.

"In a democracy, the government is the people," Milo explained. "We're people, aren't we? So we might just as well keep the money and eliminate the middleman. Frankly, I'd like to see the government get out of war altogether and leave the whole field to private industry. If we pay the government everything we owe it, we'll only be encouraging government control and discouraging other individuals from bombing their own men and planes. We'll be taking away their incentive."

Milo was correct, of course, as everyone soon agreed but a few embittered misfits like Doc Daneeka, who sulked cantankerously and muttered offensive insinuations about the morality of the whole venture until Milo mollified him with a donation, in the name of the syndicate, of a lightweight aluminum collapsible garden chair that Doc Daneeka could fold up conveniently and carry outside his tent each time Chief White Halfoat came inside his tent and carry back inside his tent each time Chief White Halfoat came out. Doc Daneeka had lost his head during Milo's bombardment; instead of running for cover, he had remained out in the open and performed his duty, slithering along the ground through shrapnel, strafing and incendiary bombs like a furtive, wily lizard from casualty to casualty, administering tourniquets, morphine, splints and sulfanilamide with a dark and doleful visage, never saying one word more than he had to and reading in each man's bluing wound a dreadful portent of his own decay. He worked himself relentlessly into exhaustion before the long night was over and came down with a sniffle the next day that sent him hurrying querulously into the medical tent to have his temperature taken by Gus and Wes and to obtain a mustard plaster and vaporizer.

Doc Daneeka tended each moaning man that night with the same glum and profound and introverted grief he showed at the airfield the day of the Avignon mission when Yossarian climbed down the few steps of his plane naked, in a state of utter shock, with Snowden smeared abundantly all over his bare heels and toes, knees, arms and fingers, and pointed inside wordlessly toward where the young radiogunner lay freezing to death on the floor beside the still younger tail-gunner who kept falling back into a dead faint each time he opened his eyes and saw Snowden dying.

Doc Daneeka draped a blanket around Yossarian's shoulders almost tenderly after Snowden had been removed from the plane and carried into an ambulance on a stretcher. He led Yossarian toward his jeep. McWatt helped, and the three drove in silence to the squadron medical tent, where McWatt and Doc Daneeka guided Yossarian inside to a chair and washed Snowden off him with cold wet balls of absorbent cotton. Doc Daneeka gave him a pill and a shot that put him to sleep for twelve hours. When Yossarian woke up and went to see him, Doc Daneeka gave him another pill and a shot that put him to sleep for another twelve hours. When Yossarian woke up again and went to see him, Doc Daneeka made ready to give him another pill and a shot.

"How long are you going to keep giving me those pills and shots?" Yossarian asked him.

"Until you feel better."

"I feel all right now."

Doc Daneeka's fragile suntanned forehead furrowed with surprise. "Then why don't you put some clothes on? Why are you walking around naked?"

"I don't want to wear a uniform any more."

Doc Daneeka accepted the explanation and put away his hypodermic syringe. "Are you sure you feel all right?"

"I feel fine. I'm just a little logy from all those pills and shots you've been giving me."

Yossarian went about his business with no clothes on all the rest of that day and was still naked late the next morning when Milo, after hunting everywhere else, finally found him sitting up a tree a small distance in back of the quaint little military cemetery at which Snowden was being buried. Milo was dressed in his customary business attire—olive-drab trousers, a fresh olive-drab shirt and tie, with one silver first lieutenant's bar gleaming on the collar, and a regulation dress cap with a stiff leather bill.

"I've been looking all over for you," Milo called up to Yossarian from the ground reproachfully.

"You should have looked for me in this tree," Yossarian answered. "I've been up here all morning."

"Come on down and taste this and tell me if it's good. It's very important."

Yossarian shook his head. He sat nude on the lowest limb of the tree and balanced himself with both hands grasping the bough directly above. He refused to budge, and Milo had no choice but to stretch both arms about the trunk in a distasteful hug and start climbing. He struggled upward clumsily with loud grunts and wheezes, and his clothes were squashed and crooked by the time he pulled himself up high enough to hook a leg over the limb and pause for breath. His dress cap was askew and in danger of falling. Milo caught it just when it began slipping. Globules of perspiration glistened like transparent pearls around his mustache and swelled like opaque blisters under his eyes. Yossarian watched him impassively. Cautiously Milo worked himself around in a half circle so that he could face Yossarian. He unwrapped tissue paper from something soft, round and brown and handed it out to Yossarian.

"Please taste this and let me know what you think. I'd like to serve it to the men."

"What is it?" asked Yossarian, and took a big bite.

"Chocolate-covered cotton."

Yossarian gagged convulsively and sprayed his big mouthful of chocolate-covered cotton right out into Milo's face. "Here, take it back!" he spouted angrily. "Jesus Christ! Have you gone crazy? You didn't even take the goddam seeds out."

"Give it a chance, will you?" Milo begged. "It can't be that bad. Is it really that bad?"

"It's even worse."

"But I've got to make the mess halls feed it to the men."

"They'll never be able to swallow it."

"They've got to swallow it," Milo ordained with dictatorial grandeur, and almost broke his neck when he let go with one arm to wave a righteous finger in the air.

"Come on out here," Yossarian invited him. "You'll be much safer, and you can see everything."

Gripping the bough above with both hands, Milo began inching his way out on the limb sideways with utmost care and apprehension. His face was rigid with tension, and he sighed with relief when he found himself seated securely beside Yossarian. He stroked the tree affectionately. "This is a pretty good tree," he observed admiringly with proprietary gratitude.

"It's the tree of life," Yossarian answered, waggling his toes, "and of knowledge of good and evil, too."

Milo squinted closely at the bark and branches. "No it isn't," he replied. "It's a chestnut tree. I ought to know. I sell chestnuts."

"Have it your way."

They sat in the tree without talking for several seconds, their legs dangling and their hands almost straight up on the bough above, the one completely nude but for a pair of crepe-soled sandals, the other completely dressed in a coarse olive-drab woolen uniform with his tie knotted tight. Milo studied Yossarian diffidently through the corner of his eye, hesitating tactfully.

"I want to ask you something," he said at last. "You don't have any clothes on. I don't want to butt in or anything, but I just want to know. Why aren't you wearing your uniform?"

"I don't want to."

Milo nodded rapidly like a sparrow pecking. "I see, I see," he stated quickly with a look of vivid confusion. "I understand perfectly. I heard Appleby and Captain Black say you had gone crazy, and I just wanted to find out." He hesitated politely again, weighing his next question. "Aren't you ever going to put your uniform on again?"

"I don't think so."

Milo nodded with spurious vim to indicate he still understood and then sat silent, ruminating gravely with troubled misgiving. A scarlet-crested bird shot by below, brushing sure dark wings against a quivering bush. Yossarian and Milo were covered in their bower by tissue-thin tiers of sloping green and largely surrounded by other gray chestnut trees and a silver spruce. The sun was high overhead in a vast sapphire-blue sky beaded with low, isolated, puffy clouds of dry and immaculate white. There was no breeze, and the leaves about them hung motionless. The shade was feathery. Everything was at peace but Milo, who straightened suddenly with a muffled cry and began pointing excitedly.

"Look at that!" he exclaimed in alarm. "Look at that! That's a funeral going on down there. That looks like the cemetery. Isn't it?"

Yossarian answered him slowly in a level voice. "They're burying that kid who got killed in my plane over Avignon the other day. Snowden."

"What happened to him?" Milo asked in a voice deadened with awe.

"He got killed."

"That's terrible," Milo grieved, and his large brown eyes filled with tears. "That poor kid. It really is terrible." He bit his trembling lip hard, and his voice rose with emotion when he continued. "And it will get even worse if the mess halls don't agree to buy my cotton. Yossarian, what's the matter with them? Don't they realize it's their syndicate? Don't they know they've all got a share?"

"Did the dead man in my tent have a share?" Yossarian demanded caustically.

"Of course he did," Milo assured him lavishly. "Everybody in the squadron has a share."

"He was killed before he even got into the squadron."

Milo made a deft grimace of tribulation and turned away. "I wish you'd stop picking on me about that dead man in your tent," he pleaded peevishly. "I told you I didn't have anything to do with killing him. Is it my fault that I saw this great opportunity to corner the market on Egyptian cotton and got us into all this trouble? Was I supposed to know there was going to be a glut? I didn't even know what a glut was in those days. An opportunity to corner a market doesn't come along very often, and I was pretty shrewd to grab the chance when I had it." Milo gulped back a moan as he saw six uniformed pallbearers lift the plain pine coffin from the ambulance and set it gently down on the ground beside the yawning gash of the freshly dug grave. "And now I can't get rid of a single penny's worth," he mourned.

Yossarian was unmoved by the fustian charade of the burial ceremony, and by Milo's crushing bereavement. The chaplain's voice floated up to him through the distance tenuously in an unintelligible, almost inaudible monotone, like a gaseous murmur. Yossarian could make out Major Major by his towering and lanky aloofness and thought he recognized Major Danby mopping his brow with a handkerchief. Major Danby had not stopped shaking since his run-in with General Dreedle. There were strands of enlisted men molded in a curve around the three officers, as inflexible as lumps of wood, and four idle gravediggers in streaked fatigues lounging indifferently on spades near the shocking, incongruous heap of loose copper-red earth. As Yossarian stared, the chaplain elevated his gaze toward Yossarian beatifically, pressed his fingers down over his eyeballs in a manner of affliction, peered upward again toward Yossarian searchingly, and bowed his head, concluding what Yossarian took to be a climactic part of the funeral rite. The four men in fatigues lifted the coffin on slings and lowered it into the grave. Milo shuddered violently.

"I can't watch it," he cried, turning away in anguish. "I just can't sit here and watch while those mess halls let my syndicate die." He gnashed his teeth and shook his head with bitter woe and resentment. "If they had any loyalty, they would buy my cotton till it hurts so that they can keep right on buying my cotton till it hurts them some more. They would build fires and burn up their underwear and summer uniforms just to create a bigger demand. But they won't do a thing. Yossarian, try eating the rest of this chocolate-covered cotton for me. Maybe it will taste delicious now."

Yossarian pushed his hand away. "Give up, Milo. People can't eat cotton."

Milo's face narrowed cunningly. "It isn't really cotton," he coaxed. "I was joking. It's really cotton candy, delicious cotton candy. Try it and see."

"Now you're lying."

"I never lie!" Milo rejoindered with proud dignity.

"You're lying now."

"I only lie when it's necessary," Milo explained defensively, averting his eyes for a moment and blinking his lashes winningly. "This stuff is better than cotton candy, really it is. It's made out of real cotton. Yossarian, you've got to help me make the men eat it. Egyptian cotton is the finest cotton in the world."

"But it's indigestible," Yossarian emphasized. "It will make them sick, don't you understand? Why don't you try living on it yourself if you don't believe me?"

"I did try," admitted Milo gloomily. "And it made me sick."

The graveyard was yellow as hay and green as cooked cabbage. In a little while the chaplain stepped back, and the beige crescent of human forms began to break up sluggishly, like flotsam. The men drifted without haste or sound to the vehicles parked along the side of the bumpy dirt road. With their heads down disconsolately, the chaplain, Major Major and Major Danby moved toward their jeeps in an ostracized group, each holding himself friendlessly several feet away from the other two.

"It's all over," observed Yossarian.

"It's the end," Milo agreed despondently. "There's no hope left. And all because I left them free to make their own decisions. That should teach me a lesson about discipline the next time I try something like this."

"Why don't you sell your cotton to the government?" Yossarian suggested casually, as he watched the four men in streaked fatigues shoveling heaping bladefuls of the copper-red earth back down inside the grave.

Milo vetoed the idea brusquely. "It's a matter of principle," he explained firmly. "The government has no business in business, and I would be the last person in the world to ever try to involve the government in a business of mine. But the business of government *is* business," he remembered alertly, and continued with elation. "Calvin Coolidge said that, and Calvin Coolidge was a President, so it must be true. And the government does have the responsibility of buying all the Egyptian cotton I've got that no one else wants so that I can make a profit, doesn't it?" Milo's face clouded almost as abruptly, and his spirits descended into a state of sad anxiety. "But how will I get the government to do it?"

"Bribe it," Yossarian said.

"Bribe it!" Milo was outraged and almost lost his balance and broke his neck again. "Shame on you!" he scolded severely, breathing virtuous fire down and upward into his rusty mustache through his billowing nostrils and prim lips. "Bribery is against the law, and you know it. But it's not against the law to make a profit, is it? So it can't be against the law for me to bribe someone in order to make a fair profit, can it? No, of course not!" He fell to brooding again, with a meek, almost pitiable distress. "But how will I know who to bribe?"

"Oh, don't you worry about that," Yossarian comforted him with a toneless snicker as the engines of the jeeps and ambulance fractured the drowsy silence and the vehicles in the rear began driving away backward. "You make the bribe big enough and they'll find you. Just make sure you do everything right out in the open. Let everyone know exactly what you want and how much you're willing to pay for it. The first time you act guilty or ashamed, you might get into trouble."

"I wish you'd come with me," Milo remarked. "I won't feel safe among people who take bribes. They're no better than a bunch of crooks."

"You'll be all right," Yossarian assured him with confidence. "If you run into trouble, just tell everybody that the security of the country requires a strong domestic Egyptian-cotton speculating industry."

"It does," Milo informed him solemnly. "A strong Egyptian-cotton speculating industry means a much stronger America."

"Of course it does. And if that doesn't work, point out the great number of American families that depend on it for income."

"A great many American families do depend on it for income."

"You see?" said Yossarian. "You're much better at it than I am. You almost make it sound true."

"It is true," Milo exclaimed with a strong trace of the old hauteur.

"That's what I mean. You do it with just the right amount of conviction."

"You're sure you won't come with me?"

Yossarian shook his head.

Milo was impatient to get started. He stuffed the remainder of the chocolate-covered cotton ball into his shirt pocket and edged his way back gingerly along the branch to the smooth gray trunk. He threw his arms about the trunk in a generous and awkward embrace and began shinnying down, the sides of his leather-soled shoes slipping constantly so that it seemed many times he would fall and injure himself. Half-way down, he changed his mind and climbed back up. Bits of tree bark stuck to his mustache, and his straining face was flushed with exertion.

"I wish you'd put your uniform on instead of going around naked that way," he confided pensively before he climbed back down again and hurried away. "You might start a trend, and then I'll never get rid of all this goldarned cotton."

J. P. DONLEAVY

from The Ginger Man

O summer of soft wind. Relieves the heart and makes living cheaper. Get that fire out in the grate. Get it out. That's better.

There's a butcher a few houses up the street. A tram goes by the window. And across the road is the most fantastic laundry with forty girls and great steaming vats. O I think they are a bunch for using just the little touch of acid.

Mr. and Mrs. Sebastian Dangerfield and their daughter, Felicity Wilton, late of Howth, are now residing at 1 Mohammed Road, The Rock, Co. Dublin.

It was decided to get out of the haunted house of Howth. But there were hesitations till the morning after the storm when Marion opened the kitchen door to get the milk and she screamed and Sebastian came running and they looked down in the mud stained sea into which had fallen the back garden and turf shed. They moved.

The new house was not new. And you didn't want to walk too fast in the front door or you'd find yourself going out the back. Mr. Egbert Skully took Mr. Dangerfield aside and said he was glad he could rent it to an American because he and his wife had worked for twenty years in Macy's Department Store and loved New York and was pleased he could find tenants like themselves. And I hope you, your wife and little one will be happy here. I know it's a little small but I think you'll like the cosy quality, ha, you look like a gentleman, Mr. Dangerfield as likes his cosy comforts, and do you play golf? O aye. But my clubs are indisposed. Having them looked over by a professional for flaws, particular about alignment you know. A very good idea, Mr. Dangerfield and perhaps my wife can give yours some recipes. Great.

Walls newly papered with brown flowers even feel soggy to the touch. And a nice brown, fourth-hand Axminster rug on the sitting-room floor and a scabrous, blue settee. The kitchen was fine but the tap and sink were out the door. Up steep narrow stairs, a closet with plate sized skylight, the conservatory. And a toilet bowl wedged between two walls, the lavatory. Tory was a great suffix in this house. And the sitting-room window two feet off the sidewalk was perfect for the neighbors passing by, so don't want to get caught with the pants down. But the tram rumbling by keeps one on one's guard.

A visit to the fuel merchant for coal to keep piled under the stairs. Marion got crates and covered them with table cloths for color and respectability. And my special maps one or two of which are rare and old. The one I have of a cemetery I keep under thick glass. And got the card table for a desk under the window. The laundry girls will take my mind off the awful grind of studying. They come out twice a day, hair in curlers and breasts like needles in these American uplift bras. Think the Bishop had something to say about that and rightly too. Then watch them line up for the tram, a row of steamed white faces. And some of them giving a giggle in this direction at the madman behind the curtain.

Facing the summer ahead. Living in this little house was calm. No drinking and minding the baba when Marion was off to shop. Had a cup of beef tea in the morning. Also see a rather pleasant creature up there in the window. Catch her looking in here with rather large brown eyes, no smiles or giggles. A little disdain, her dark hair straight and thick. And I think I see intelligence, a little embarrassing that look. Retreat into the kitchen. Most exciting.

Made a little case and filled it with books of law, a short life of Blessed Oliver Plunket and others on birds. Bottom shelf for business magazines for the big days ahead. And then a section for my extensive collection, which, God forgive me, I stole from Catholic Churches. But I did it because I needed strength in paupery. My favorites are *This Thing Called Love, Drink Is A Curse,* and *Happiness in Death.*

The first morning tram almost shakes one to the floor

and Felicity gives the twisted cry from the conservatory. Growl back to sleep. Pull the legs up in the fetal crouch. Marion wearing my underwear. Sometimes the sun would sneak in. Then Marion beating barefoot on the linoleum. Entreaties. O do get up. Don't leave me to do everything every morning. In my heart where no one else can hear me, I was saying, now for God's sake, Marion, be a good Britisher and get down there in that little nest of a kitchen and buzz on the coffee like a good girl and would you, while you're at it, kind of brown up a few pieces of bread and I wouldn't mind if maybe there was just the suggestion of bacon on it, only a suggestion, and have it all ready on the table and then I'll come down and act the good husband with, ah darling good morning, how are you, you're looking lovely this morning darling and younger every morning. A great one that last. But I come down martyred and mussed, feeble and fussed, heart and soul covered in cement.

But later in the morning great things were to be seen. Sound of horses on the cobble stones. Then up to the bedroom to look down in the street. These sleek black animals glistening in soft rain. Heads high, driving slits of steam in the morning air. Sometimes I see through the little glass windows, a lily on a pine box. Take me with you too. And I can't help murmuring from memory poems I read in the *Evening Mail:*

> *Sleep thy last sleep,*
> *Free from care and sorrow,*
> *Rest where none weep,*
> *And we too, shall follow.*

And I see the grinning red faces popping out the windows of the cab, radiant with the importance of the dead. Hats being tipped along the road and hands moving in the quick sign of the cross. Whisky passed from hand to hand. Green, greedy mouth is dead. A fiddle across the fields. Mushrooms fatten in the warm September rain. Gone away.

Then time to go for the paper. And back with it to the lavatory. Between the green peeling walls. Always feel I'm going to get stuck. One morning there was sunshine and I was feeling great. Sitting in there grunting and groaning, looking over the news, and then reach up and pull the chain. Downstairs in the kitchen, Marion screamed.

"I say, Marion, what is it?"

"For God's sake, stop it, stop it, Sebastian, you fool. What have you done?"

Moving with swift irritability down the narrow stairs, stumbling into the kitchen at the bottom. Perhaps things have gotten too much for Marion and she's gone mad.

"You idiot, Sebastian, look at me, look at baby's things."

Marion trembling in the middle of the kitchen floor covered with strands of wet toilet paper and fecal matter. From a gaping patch in the ceiling poured water, plaster and excrement.

"God's miserable teeth."

"O damnable, damnable. Do something, you fool."

"For the love of Jesus."

Sebastian stalking away.

"How dare you walk away, you damnable rotter. This is horrible and I can't bear any more."

Marion broke into sobs, slammed into silence with the front door.

Walking past the parking lot, down the little hill to the station. Stand by this wall here and watch the trains go by. Just take a crap and look what happens. This damn Skully probably put in rubber pipes. Three pounds a week for a rat hole, with brown swamp grass on the walls and cardboard furniture. And Marion has to be standing right under it. Couldn't she hear it coming? And the sun's gone in and it looks like rain. Better get back to the house or it'll weaken my position. Get her a little present, a fashion magazine filled with richery.

Marion sitting in the easy chair sewing. Pausing at the door, testing the silence.

"I'm sorry, Marion."

Marion head bent. Sebastian tendering his gift.

"I really am sorry. Look at me, I've got a present for you. It's hot tamale with ink dressing, see."

"O."

"Nice?"

"Yes."

"Like the gold teeth of God?"

"Don't spoil it now."

"My little Marion. I'm such a bastard. I tell you the whole thing up there is just a bunch of roots."

"I'll have something to read in bed."

"I'm an incredible pig, Marion."

"Aren't these suits nice."

"Don't you hear me, Marion? I'm a pig."

"Yes, but I wish we were rich and had money. I want to travel. If we could only travel."

"Let me kiss you, Marion, at least."

Marion arose, embracing him with blonde arms, driving her long groin against his and her tongue deep into his mouth.

Marion you're good underneath it all and not a bad feel. Just irritable at times. Now go in there and cook the dinner. And I'll relax here in the chair and read my *Evening Mail*. I see listed conscience money. Great thing, the conscience. And letters about emigration and women who marry for quids. And here's a letter about Blessed Oliver Plunket. We went up to see him there in the St. Peter's Church, Drogheda. A decapitated, two hundred and sixty year old head. Made me feel hushed. Gray, pink and battered and a glint of dead, bared teeth in the candle light. Charwoman told me to touch it, touch it now, sir, for it's great for luck. I put my finger, afeared, into the mouldy nose hole, for you can't have too much luck these days.

Now I see them across the street coming out of the laundry. Pouring into the road, faces lining up for the tram. There's the girl with the brown eyes and dark hair, her face colorless but for handsome lips. Her legs in lisle stockings and feet in army surplus boots. Hatless and hair in a bun. Goes to the newsboy, calves knotting softly on the backs of her legs. Tucks the paper under her arm and waits in the queue.

In my heart I know she isn't a virgin, but perhaps childless with pink buds for nipples or even if they're sucked and dark I don't mind. Wears a green scarf around her nice neck. Necks should be white and long with a blue nervous vein twitching with the nervousness of life in general. My good gracious savior, she's looking over here. Hide? What am I? A scoundrel, a sneak? Not a bit. Face her. You're lovely. Absolutely lovely. Put my face on your spring breasts. Take you to Paris and tie your hair in knots with summer leaves.

"Sebastian, it's ready, do bring in the chair."

In the kitchen cutting a thick slice off the loaf, scraping butter out of a cup.

"Sebastian, what about the toilet?"

"What about it?"

"Who's going to fix it?"

"Marion, I beg of you, this is dinner time. Do you want to give me ulcers?"

"Why don't you take some responsibility?"

"After dinner. Don't drive me up the wall over Irish plumbing, it's new to the country and the pipes got mixed."

"But who'll pay?"

"Skully out of his little gold egg."

"And the smell, Sebastian. What can we do about the smell?"

"It's just healthy shit."

"How dare you use that ugly word."

"Shit's shit, Marion, even on judgment day."

"It's foul and I won't have it said in the same house as Felicity."

"She'll hear it and also in the matter of foulness I'll see to it she's laid before she's fifteen."

Marion silently seized. Putting egg shell in the coffee to make it settle. Notice her fingers bitten. She moves through the mess.

"All right, Marion, take it easy. It's just adjustment. Got to get used to it here."

"Why must you be so raw?"

"The mean meat in me."

"Be sincere. You weren't like this before we came to Ireland. This vulgar filthy country."

"Easy now."

"Children running barefoot in the streets in the middle of winter and men wagging their things at you from doorways. Disgusting."

"Untruths. Lies."

"They're a foul lot. I understand now why they're only fit to be servants."

"I say, Marion, a little bitterness?"

"You know it's true. Look at that frightful O'Keefe and his dirty ideas. America doesn't seem to help. Brings the worst out in them. He's not even fit to be a servant."

"I think Kenneth's a gentleman in every respect. Have you ever heard him fart? Now, have you?"

"Absolutely frightful rot. One has only to watch him leering over the cat when it's in heat to see he's dreadfully base. When he comes into the room I feel he's criminally assaulting me in his mind."

"It's legal."

"It's the revolting lechery of an Irish peasant. And he tries to give the impression of good breeding. Watch him eating. It's infuriating. Grabs everything. That first time we had him to dinner he just came in as if we were servants and proceeded to eat even before I had time to sit down. And pulling hunks out of the bread, how can you be blind to these things?"

"Now, now, a little patience with the people who have given your country a Garden of Eden to play in, make your fires and serve your tea."

"I wish we had stayed in England. You could have waited for Oxford or Cambridge. And we could have at least maintained a measure of dignity."

"I'll admit there's not much of that."

Long limbed Marion settled in the chair. What makes you so tall and slender. You raise your eyelids and cross your legs with something I like and wear sexless shoes with sexiness. And Marion I'll say this for you, you're not blatant. And when we get our house in the West with the Kerry cattle out on the hills sucking up the grass and I'm Dangerfield Q.C., things will be fine again.

A tram pounding by the window, grinding, swaying and rattling on its tracks to Dalkey. A comforting sound. Maps shaking on the wall. Ireland a country of toys. And maybe I ought to go over to Marion on the couch. We're experimenting with marriage. Got to find the contraceptives or else another screaming mouth for milk. The brown-eyed girl in the laundry is about twenty-five. Marion sucking on her false teeth again, I think it must be a sign of wanting it.

In the bedroom, Dangerfield rubbing stockinged feet on the cold linoleum. And the sound of Marion using the piss pot behind Skully's genuine Ming dynasty screen. And a little tug at these tattered shades for the privacy. Even in this great Catholic country you've got to keep covered, you know, or they watch you undress, but mind you, the Protestants use a field glass.

And Marion clutching the hem of her dress and drawing it over her shifting shoulders. She said there was only thirty shillings left.

"Our good accents and manners will see us right. Didn't you know, Marion, they can't put Protestants in jail?"

"You've no responsibility and to have my child raised

among a lot of savage Irish and be branded with a brogue
for the rest of her life. Pass me my cream, please."

Sebastian passing the cream, smiling and waving his feet
from the edge of the bed. Letting his body fall with a squeal
of springs and looking at the patches of pink in the ceiling.

Marion a bit upset and confused. Difficult for her. She
was breaking. Isn't as strong as me, led a sheltered life.
Maybe shouldn't have married me. Matter, all of it, of time.
Pumping it around and around, air in, air out and then it all
goes like the shutters of a collapsing house. Starts and ends
in antiseptic smell. Like to feel the end would be like
closing leaves of honeysuckle, pressing out a last fragrance
in the night but that only happens to holy men. Find them
in the morning with a smile across the lips and bury them in
plain boxes. But I want a rich tomb of Vermont marble in
Woodlawn Cemetery, with automatic sprinkler and ever-
greens. If they get you in the medical school they hang you
up by the ears. Never leave me unclaimed, I beg of you. Don't
hang me all swollen, knees pressing the red nates of others
where they come in to see if I'm fat or lean and all of us
stabbed to death on the Bowery. Kill you in the tenement
streets and cover you in flowers and put in the juice. By
God, you hulking idiots, keep the juice away from me. I'm
too busy to die.

"Marion, do you ever think of death?"

"No."

"Marion, do you ever think you're going to die?"

"I say, Sebastian, would you mind awfully stopping that
sort of talk. You're in that nasty mood."

"Not at all."

"You are. Coming up here every morning to watch the
funerals of these wretched people. Dreadful and sordid. I
think you get a perverse pleasure out of it."

"Beyond this vale of tears, there is a life above, unmeas-
ured by the flight of years and all that life is love."

"You think you're frightening me with these sinister airs
of yours. I find them only boring and they tend to make
you repulsive."

"What?"

"Yes, they do."

"For the love of Oliver, look at me. Look at my eyes. Go
ahead, come on."

"I don't want to look in your eyes."

"Honest globes they are."

"You can't talk seriously about anything."

"I just asked you about death. Want to know how you feel, really get to know you. Or maybe you think this is for ever."

"Rubbish. You think it's for ever, I know you do. You're not as flippant as this in the mornings, I notice."

"Takes me a few hours to adapt. Snap out of the dream."

"And you scream."

"What?"

"You were yelling a few nights ago, how do I get out of this. And another time you were screaming, what's that white thing in the corner, take it away."

Dangerfield holding his belly, laughing on the squeaking springs.

"You can laugh, but I think there's something serious at the root of it."

"What's at the root? Can't you see I'm mad. Can't you see? Look. See. Madness. E. I'm mad."

Sebastian ogled and wagged his tongue.

"Stop it. Always willing to clown but never to do anything useful."

Dangerfield watched from the bed as she flexed her long arms behind her back and her breasts fell from the cups of her brassiere, tan nipples harding in the cold air. Red line on her shoulder left by the strap. Stepping wearily out of her underpants, facing the mirror and rubbing white cream into her hands and face. Little brown strands growing round the nipples. You've often said, Marion, about giving it the wax treatment but I like them that way after all.

Sebastian quietly stepping from the bed approaching the naked body. Pressing his fists against her buttock and she pushes his hands away.

"I don't like you touching me there."

And kissing her on the back of the neck. Wet the skin with the tongue and the long blonde hair gets in the mouth. Marion taking the blue nightdress from the nail. Sebastian stripping and sitting naked on the edge of the bed, taking white fluff out of the navel, and doubling himself, plucking the congealed dirt from between his toes.

"Sebastian, I wish you'd take a bath."

"Kills the personality."

"You were so clean when I first knew you."

"Given up the cleanliness for a life of the spirit. Preparation for another and better world. Hardly take offence at a little scruffiness. Clean soul's my motto. Take off your nightie."

"Where are they?"

"Under my shirts."

"And the vaseline?"

"Behind the books on the box."

Marion ripping the silver paper. Americans great for packages. Wrap anything up. And she draws the opening of her nightdress back from her shoulders, letting it fall to her feet and folding it carefully across the books. She kneels on the bed. What are other men like, do they grunt and groan, are they all curved and circumcised, with or without. She climbs into bed, a soft voice.

"Let's do it the way we used to in Yorkshire."

"Umn."

"Do you still like my breasts the way they are?"

"Umn."

"Tell me things, Sebastian, talk to me. I want to know."

Sebastian rolled near, pressing the long, blonde body to his, thinking of a world outside beating drums below the window in the rain. All slipping on the cobble stones. And standing aside as a tram full of Bishops rumbles past, who hold up sacred hands in blessing. Marion's hand tightening and touching my groin. Ginny Cupper took me in her car out to the spread fields of Indiana. Parking near the edge of the woods and walking out into the sunny rows of corn, waving seeds to a yellow horizon. She wore a white blouse and a gray patch of sweat under her arms and the shadow of her nipples was grey. We were rich. So rich we could never die. Ginny laughed and laughed, white saliva on her teeth lighting up the deep red of her mouth, fed the finest food in the world. Ginny was afraid of nothing. She was young and old. Her brown arms and legs swinging in wild optimism, beautiful in all their parts. She danced on the long hood of her crimson Cadillac, and watching her, I thought that God must be female. She leaped into my arms and knocked me to the ground and screamed into my mouth. Heads pressed in the hot Indiana soil and pinned me in a cross. A crow cawed into the white sun and my sperm spurted into the world. Ginny had driven her long Cadillac through the guard rails of a St. Louis bridge and her car shone like a clot of blood in the mud and murk of the Mississippi. We were all there in the summer silence of Suffolk, Virginia, when the copper casket was gently placed in the cool marble vault. I smoked a cigarette and crushed it out on the black and white squares of the tomb. In the stagnant emptiness of the train station after the cars were gone, I walked into the women's toilet and saw the phallic obscenities on the wooden doors and gray walls. I wonder if people will think I'm a lecher. Ginny had gardenias in her lovely brown hair. I hear the train, Marion's breath in my ear. My stomach's shaking, my last strength. The world's silent. Crops have stopped growing. Now they grow again.

VLADIMIR NABOKOV

Scenes from the Life of a Double Monster

Some years ago Dr. Fricke asked Lloyd and me a question that I shall try to answer now. With a dreamy smile of scientific delectation he stroked the fleshy cartilaginous band uniting us—*omphalopagus diaphragmo-xiphodidymus,* as Pancoast has dubbed a similar case—and wondered if we could recall the very first time either of us, or both, realized the peculiarity of our condition and destiny. All Lloyd could remember was the way our Grandfather Ibrahim (or Ahim, or Ahem—irksome lumps of dead sounds to the ear of today!) would touch what the doctor was touching and call it a bridge of gold. I said nothing.

Our childhood was spent atop a fertile hill above the Black Sea on our grandfather's farm near Karaz. His youngest daughter, rose of the East, gray Ahem's pearl (if so, the old scoundrel might have taken better care of her) had been raped in a roadside orchard by our anonymous sire and had died soon after giving birth to us—of sheer horror and grief, I imagine. One set of rumors mentioned a Hungarian peddler; another favored a German collector of birds or some member of his expedition—his taxidermist, most likely. Dusky, heavily necklaced aunts, whose voluminous clothes smelled of rose oil and mutton, attended with ghoulish zest to the wants of our monstrous infancy.

Soon neighboring hamlets learned the astounding news and began delegating to our farm various inquisitive strangers. On feast days you could see them laboring up the slopes of our hill, like pilgrims in bright-colored pictures. There was a shepherd seven feet tall, and a small bald man with glasses, and soldiers, and the lengthening shadows of cypresses. Children came too, at all times, and were shooed away by our jealous nurses; but almost daily some black-eyed, cropped-haired youngster in dark-patched, faded-blue pants would manage to worm his way through the dogwood, the honeysuckle, the twisted Judas trees, into the cobbled court with its old rheumy fountain where little Lloyd and Floyd (we had other names then, full of corvine aspirates—but no matter) sat quietly munching dried apricots under a whitewashed wall. Then, suddenly, the aitch would see an eye, the Roman two a one, the scissors a knife.

There can be, of course, no comparison between this impact of knowledge, disturbing as it may have been, and the emotional shock my mother received (by the way, what clean bliss there is in this deliberate use of the possessive singular!). She must have been aware that she was being delivered of twins; but when she learned, as no doubt she did, that the twins were conjoined ones—what did she experience then? With the kind of unrestrained, ignorant, passionately communicative folks that surrounded us, the highly vocal household just beyond the limits of her tumbled bed must, surely, have told her at once that something had gone dreadfully wrong; and one can be certain that her sister, in the frenzy of their fright and compassion, showed her the double baby. I am not saying that a mother cannot love such a double thing —and forget in this love the dark dews of its unhallowed origin; I only think that the mixture of revulsion, pity, and a mother's love was too much for her. Both components of the double series before her staring eyes were healthy, handsome little components, with a silky fair fuzz on their violet-pink skulls, and well-formed rubbery arms and legs that moved like the many limbs of some wonderful sea animal. Each was eminently normal, but together they formed a monster. Indeed, it is strange to think that the presence of a mere band of tissue, a flap of flesh not much longer than a lamb's liver, should be able to transform joy, pride, tenderness, adoration, gratitude to God into horror and despair.

In our own case everything was far simpler. Adults were much too different from us in all respects to afford any analogy, but our first coeval visitor was to me a mild revelation. While Lloyd placidly contemplated the awestruck child of seven or eight who was peering at us from under a humped and likewise peering fig tree, I remember appreciating in full the essential difference between the newcomer and me. He cast a short blue shadow on the ground, and so did I; but in addition to that sketchy, and flat, and unstable companion which he and I owed to the sun and which vanished in dull weather I possessed yet another shadow, a palpable reflection of my corporal self, that I always had by me, at my left side, whereas my visitor had somehow managed to lose his, or had unhooked it and left it at home. Linked Lloyd and Floyd were complete and normal; he was neither.

But perhaps, in order to elucidate these matters as thoroughly as they deserve, I should say something of still earlier recollections. Unless adult emotions stain past ones, I think I can vouch for the memory of a faint disgust. By virtue of our anterior duplexity, we lay originally front to front, joined at our common navel, and my face in those first years of our existence was constantly brushed by my twin's hard nose and wet lips. A tendency to throw our heads back and avert our faces as much as possible was a natural reaction to those bothersome contacts. The great flexibility of our band of union allowed us to assume reciprocally a more or less lateral position, and as we learned to walk we waddled about in this side-by-side attitude, which must have seemed more strained than it really was, making us look, I suppose, like a pair of drunken dwarfs supporting each other. For a long time we kept reverting in sleep to our fetal position; but whenever the discomfort it engendered woke us up, we would again jerk our faces away, in regardant revulsion, with a double wail.

I insist that at three or four our bodies obscurely disliked their clumsy conjunctions, while our minds did not question its normalcy. Then, before we could have become mentally aware of its drawbacks, physical intuition discovered means of tempering them, and thereafter we hardly gave them a thought. All our movements became a judicious compromise between the common and the particular. The pattern of acts prompted by this or that mutual urge formed a kind of gray, evenly woven, generalized background against which the discrete impulse, his or mine, followed a brighter and sharper course; but (guided as it were by the warp of the background pattern) it never went athwart the common weave or the other twin's whim.

I am speaking at present solely of our childhood, when nature could not yet afford to have us undermine our hard-won vitality by any conflict between us. In later years I have had occasion to regret that we did not perish or had not been surgically separated, before we left that initial stage at which an ever-present rhythm, like some kind of remote tom-tom beating in the jungle of our nervous system, was alone responsible for the regulation of our movements. When, for example, one of us was about to stoop to possess himself of a pretty daisy and the other, at exactly the same moment, was on the point of stretching up to pluck a ripe fig, individual success depended upon whose movement happened to conform to the current ictus of our common and continuous rhythm, whereupon, with a very brief, chorealike shiver, the interrupted gesture of one twin would be swallowed and dissolved in the enriched ripple of the other's completed action. I say "enriched" because the ghost of the unpicked flowers somehow seemed to be also there, pulsating between the fingers that closed upon the fruit.

There might be a period of weeks and even months when the guiding beat was much more often on Lloyd's side than on mine, and then a period might follow when I would be on top of the wave; but I cannot recall any time in our childhood when frustration or success in these matters provoked in either of us resentment or pride.

Somewhere within me, however, there must have been some sensitive cell wondering at the curious fact of a force that would suddenly sweep me away from the object of a casual desire and drag me to other, uncoveted things that were thrust into the sphere of my will instead of being consciously reached for and enveloped by its tentacles. So, as I watched this or that chance child which was watching Lloyd and me, I remember pondering a twofold problem: first, whether, perhaps, a single bodily state had more advantages than ours possessed; and second, whether *all* other children were single. It occurs to me now that quite often problems puzzling me were twofold: possibly a trickle of Lloyd's cerebration penetrated my mind and one of the two linked problems was his.

When greedy Grandfather Ahem decided to show us to visitors for money, among the flocks that came there was always some eager rascal who wanted to hear us talk to each other. As happens with primitive minds, he demanded that his ears corroborate what his eyes saw. Our folks bullied us into gratifying such desires and could not understand what was so distressful about them. We could have pleaded shyness; but the truth was that we never really *spoke* to each other, even when we were alone, for the brief broken grunts of infrequent expostulation that we sometimes exchanged (when, for instance, one had just cut his foot and had had it bandaged and the other wanted to go paddling in the brook) could hardly pass for a dialogue. The communication of simple essential sensations we performed wordlessly: shed leaves riding the stream of our shared blood. Thin thoughts also managed to slip through and travel between us. Richer ones each kept to himself, but even then there occurred odd phenomena. This is why I suspect that despite his calmer nature, Lloyd was struggling with the same new realities that were puzzling me. He forgot much when he grew up. I have forgotten nothing.

Not only did our public expect us to talk, it also wanted us to play together. Dolts! They derived quite a kick from having us match wits at checkers or *muzla*. I suppose had we happened to be opposite-sex twins they would have made us commit incest in their presence. But since mutual games were no more customary with us than conversation, we suffered subtle torments when obliged to go through the cramped motions of bandying a ball somewhere between our breastbones or making believe to wrest a stick from each other. We drew wild applause by running around the yard with our arms around each other's shoulders. We could jump and whirl.

A salesman of patent medicine, a bald little fellow in a dirty-white Russian blouse, who knew some Turkish and English, taught us sentences in these languages; and then we had to demonstrate our ability to a fascinated audience. Their ardent faces still pursue me in my nightmares, for they come whenever my dream producer needs supers. I see again the gigantic bronze-faced shepherd in multi-colored rags, the soldiers from Karaz, the one-eyed hunchbacked Armenian tailor (a monster in his own right), the giggling girls, the sighing old women, the children, the young people in Western clothes—burning eyes, white teeth, black gaping mouths; and, of course, Grandfather Ahem, with his nose of yellow ivory and his beard of gray wool, directing the proceedings or counting the soiled paper money and wetting his big thumb. The linguist, he of the embroidered blouse and bald

head, courted one of my aunts but kept watching Ahem en-
viously through his steel-rimmed spectacles.

By the age of nine, I knew quite clearly that Lloyd and I
presented the rarest of freaks. This knowledge provoked in
me neither any special elation nor any special shame; but
once a hysterical cook, a mustached woman, who had taken
a great liking to us and pitied our plight, declared with an
atrocious oath that she would, then and there, slice us free
by means of a shiny knife that she suddenly flourished (she
was at once overpowered by our grandfather and one of our
newly acquired uncles); and after that incident I would often
dally with an indolent daydream, fancying myself somehow
separated from poor Lloyd, who somehow retained his mon-
sterhood.

I did not care for that knife business, and anyway the
manner of separation remained very vague; but I distinctly
imagined the sudden melting away of my shackles and the
feeling of lightness and nakedness that would ensue. I imagined myself climbing over the fence—a fence with bleached
skulls of farm animals that crowned its pickets—and descending toward the beach. I saw myself leaping from boulder to
boulder and diving into the twinkling sea, and scrambling
back onto the shore and scampering about with other naked
children. I dreamed of this at night—saw myself fleeing from
my grandfather and carrying away with me a toy, or a kit-
ten, or a little crab pressed to my left side. I saw myself
meeting poor Lloyd, who appeared to me in my dream hobbling along, hopelessly joined to a hobbling twin while I was
free to dance around them and slap them on their humble
backs.

I wonder if Lloyd had similar visions. It has been suggested by doctors that we sometimes pooled our minds when
we dreamed. One gray-blue morning he picked up a twig and
drew a ship with three masts in the dust. I had just seen myself drawing that ship in the dust of a dream I had dreamed
the preceding night.

An ample black shepherd's cloak covered our shoulders,
and, as we squatted to the ground, all but our heads and
Lloyd's hand was concealed within its falling folds. The sun
had just risen and the sharp March air was like layer upon
layer of semitransparent ice through which the crooked Judas
trees in rough bloom made blurry spots of purplish pink. The

long low white house behind us, full of fat women and their foul-smelling husbands, was fast asleep. We did not say anything; we did not even look at each other; but, throwing his twig away, Lloyd put his right arm around my shoulder, as he always did when he wished both of us to walk fast; and with the edge of our common raiment trailing among dead weeds, while pebbles kept running from under our feet, we made our way toward the alley of cypresses that led down to the shore.

It was our first attempt to visit the sea that we could see from our hilltop softly glistening afar and leisurely, silently breaking on glossy rocks. I need not strain my memory at this point to place our stumbling flight at a definite turn in our destiny. A few weeks before, on our twelfth birthday, Grandfather Ibrahim had started to toy with the idea of sending us in the company of our newest uncle on a six-month tour through the country. They kept haggling about the terms, and had quarreled and even fought, Ahem getting the upper hand.

We feared our grandfather and loathed Uncle Novus. Presumably, after a dull forlorn fashion (knowing nothing of life, but being dimly aware that Uncle Novus was endeavoring to cheat Grandfather) we felt we should try to do something in order to prevent a showman from trundling us around in a moving prison, like apes or eagles; or perhaps we were prompted merely by the thought that this was our last chance to enjoy by ourselves our small freedom and do what we were absolutely forbidden to do: go beyond a certain picket fence, open a certain gate.

We had no trouble in opening that rickety gate, but did not manage to swing it back into its former position. A dirty-white lamb, with amber eyes and a carmine mark painted upon its hard flat forehead, followed us for a while before getting lost in the oak scrub. A little lower but still far above the valley, we had to cross the road that circled around the hill and connected our farm with the highway running along the shore. The thudding of hoofs and the rasping of wheels came descending upon us; and we dropped, cloak and all, behind a bush. When the rumble subsided, we crossed the road and continued along a weedy slope. The silvery sea gradually concealed itself behind cypresses and remnants of old stone walls. Our black cloak began to feel hot and heavy but still we persevered under its protection, being afraid that otherwise some passer-by might notice our infirmity.

We emerged upon the highway, a few feet from the audible sea—and there, waiting for us under a cypress, was a carriage we knew, a cartlike affair on high wheels, with Uncle Novus in the act of getting down from the box. Crafty, dark, ambitious, unprincipled little man! A few minutes before, he had caught sight of us from one of the galleries of our grandfather's house and had not been able to resist the temptation of taking advantage of an escapade which miraculously allowed him to seize us without any struggle or outcry. Swearing at the two timorous horses, he roughly helped us into the cart. He pushed our heads down and threatened to hurt us if we attempted to peep from under our cloak. Lloyd's arm was still around my shoulder, but a jerk of the cart shook it off. Now the wheels were crunching and rolling. It was some time before we realized that our driver was not taking us home.

Twenty years have passed since that gray spring morning, but it is much better preserved in my mind than many a later event. Again and again I run it before my eyes like a strip of cinematic film, as I have seen great jugglers do when reviewing their acts. So I review all the stages and circumstances and incidental details of our abortive flight—the initial shiver, the gate, the lamb, the slippery slope under our clumsy feet. To the thrushes we flushed we must have presented an extraordinary sight, with that black cloak around us and our two shorn heads on thin necks sticking out of it. The heads turned this way and that, warily, as at last the shoreline highway was reached. If at that moment some adventurous stranger had stepped onto the shore from his boat in the bay, he would have surely experienced a thrill of ancient enchantment to find himself confronted by a gentle mythological monster in a landscape of cypresses and white stones. He would have worshiped it, he would have shed sweet tears. But, alas, there was nobody to greet us there save that worried crook, our nervous kidnaper, a small doll-faced man wearing cheap spectacles, one glass of which was doctored with a bit of tape.

Ithaca, 1950.

CHARLES SIMMONS

from Powdered Eggs

Why didn't you tell me your mother was Jewish? With a Protestant father you must have had the same kind of deal I had. I'm not upset that you're such a sly one, I'm upset over the missed opportunities. A million times I could have said Some of my best friend is Jewish. Seriously, however, if I ever expressed any anti-semitic sentiments to you I want you to know that I meant every one of them. I didn't tell you, but Mary showed up at the funeral home. A right nice geste, I thought. I mean, she didn't know my father particularly. So we went out and had a drink afterward, and all the old thing came back. She is the third-most-beautiful girl I've ever seen. You know how I met her? In second-year high school I was the villain in the annual play, and between acts we all amused ourselves by peeking through the curtain and appraising the quiff in the audience. Up in a box was an assemblage of bright Irish-faced girls. Funny, I say that now, then that's all there was. If it wasn't a bright Irish-faced girl it was invisible. O there were sullen exotic Jewish girls, but one viewed them and was viewed by them with suspicion, and Protestant girls didn't seem interested or interesting. Fantasy directed you to the immaculate rosy mick, who you were sure ached as you did for carnal release. You just knew that she too lay abed at nights with the feminine equivalent of the implacable cock, seeking, seeking. She didn't, of course, but since girls never talked about themselves sexually you projected your own feelings into them, and you had the sense that she was locked, like yourself, against communicating the great need to anyone who could do something about it. Who knew then that girls are different creatures? Who knew that their tiny heads are full of flowers, dresses, silver service and a strong man standing by to kill spiders, make money, escort them to social functions, and occasionally in the darkness of the marriage bed kiss them on the cheek? Who knew then that just as the way to a man's heart is through his genital, the way to a woman's genital is through her heart? Don't tell me you did. All right, but if you did, it's because you were a Protestant Jew bastard. This is information they don't give out in Catholic grammar schools, where as far as the nuns are concerned, everyone, male or female, is dying to screw or at least play with himself. Grammar school was one long series of cautions. Keep your hands out of your pockets, don't linger in the bathtub, avoid dirty movies, dirty magazines, dirty books, dirty jokes and, most of all, provocative girls. Where the hell were the provocative girls, we all wanted to know. Anyway, I was peeking through the curtain, and there in the box, among the bright Irish faces, was a great bright Irish face. I see these great faces every now and then, in a bus, on the street, clerking in a department store. I've seen them all my life, but I never got to know one before. I mean, what are you going to do, walk up and say Miss, you have a great face? Well, it took me a half-hour to get the makeup off, but there in the lobby on the way out, being entertained in high style by an usher (a creepy guy who didn't get a part in the play) was the great face with her friends. The usher was big-dealing it as best he could from his ignoble station, and he called me over because I was an actor, put his arm around me and introduced me as if he was my proud father. Well, it turned out that the great face belonged to a senior in a local Catholic girls' school. Now, is there a longer distance than exists between a girl senior and a boy sophomore? Ah, but remember, I had been in the play, I had been the villain, and she accepted my invitation to go on the school boat ride. Since then I have anticipated parting other legs, grabbing other asses, but the month that separated that night from the day of the boat ride was the most expectant of my life. During the month I recalled only that she had a face you could swim in, and when I finally saw her again I was not disappointed. Tall and haughty with honey hair. Large round blue eyes and a perfect mouth, one of whose corners turned down and the other up when she smiled. And what a nose! It had a little bump from breaking it when she was a kid, which gave her that last touch of class. One of the guys on the boat ride asked me if she was my sister, and I nearly died with pride. Later I used to daydream about her really being my sister and me being in love with her nonetheless and crawling into her bed at night. So you can see, this was not a healthy relationship. The rest you've heard, up and down, in and out. After a couple of years, when I discovered that her silences were not signs of deference to my wisdom but simple incomprehension, things became more difficult. But the great face remained, and the great face came to the funeral home. We've been out three times since then. Once we went to see a revival of La Dolce Vita, which I thought was tremendous and she thought was dirty. The second time I took her to an all-Mozart concert, which she said she liked but didn't. And the last time, which was two nights ago, we went to confession together. I mean, need I say more? Well, I will say more. A year or so ago I had reached the stage where if she'd listen to me I'd propose. It was like saying hello. Mary, dear heart, how have you been, will you marry me? I don't even know if I meant it. I'd ask, I think, with the idea that if she said yes, then I'd decide if I really wanted to. Not that there seemed to be much chance of that. I can only marry a Catholic, she'd say, a practicing Catholic. And you don't even try, you're not even interested, she'd add. How can I try, I'd ask, can I try to believe that peaches are blue? She didn't seem to get this. Say one Hail Mary every day, that's all I ask, just go through the motions, and grace will come. But I don't believe in grace, I don't believe in Hail Marys. Nonetheless, will you say the words? But I don't believe anybody's listening. At which she'd sigh a rattling sigh. All right, I'll say the words, I'll say the words. And she didn't understand me, I didn't want to be forgiven my sins or attain sanctifying grace or abide forever in the kingdom of heaven. The thought of never experiencing the presence of God did not fill me with a tragic sense of loss. All I wanted was to hold this beautiful Irish-faced girl in my arms. But I kept my promise. Hail Mary, full of grace! the Lord is with thee, blessed art thou among women, and blessed is the fruit of thy womb, Jesus. Holy Mary, Mother of God, pray for us sinners, now and at the hour of our death. Amen. And when I said it I thought that that Mary, whoever she is, wherever she is, is a bright Irish-faced girl like this

Mary, perverted into religiosity by some crabbed rabbi. Hello Venus, full of juice! Cupid is with thee; blessed art thou among lovers, and blessed are the uses of thy womb, squeeze us. Sweetest Venus, Mother of Love, lay for us sinners, now and at the point of climax. Amen. That's my prayer. Anyway, she started it again at the funeral home and was at it every date since. If I go to confession, that will be making an honest effort, and she'd agree to be engaged. Suppose it doesn't work, I said. Suppose what doesn't work? Suppose I open my heart to grace and grace doesn't enter therein, what then? She'd be engaged to me anyhow, she said, because I tried. But there was about her smile when she said it a quality that meant such an eventuality was impossible. How could I open my heart to grace and grace not enter? God is ready with great syringes of grace, looking for the slightest aperture. Well, the last time I went to confession I had been fourteen. I was laying my hand on my gun and not telling it, and the rules of the game were that if you went to confession and withheld a mortal sin you were in effect lying and thereby committing another mortal sin. So at fourteen I decided it was better to break the vicious circle and quit altogether. What a relief that was! I remember the day I made up my mind to chuck it. I was on my way to church, inventing sins to tell. Inventing them, like I cursed twice, Father, I was mean to my friend once, I took a dollar from my mother's purse, I committed the sin of pride by thinking I was smarter than everybody at a party, Father. Anything but the real thing. So I quit, and here I was now, ready to sink back into the whirlpool, begin again the endless alternation of sin and forgiveness. When the hell is it that you can live at peace with the Church? If you're not married, what do you do with your whacker, that tingles at every thigh emerging from a taxi, that as you crawl under the covers at night fills unprovoked with bloody blood, asking dumbly for shelter? And if you marry, if you do the bit, what then? They demand that you impregnate as you ejaculate. OK if you're rich, but suppose you're only a former writer at MUI? I figure the only way to be a good Catholic is to be rich, sterile, impotent, inhibitedly queer, or old. Old is best, old but with a wild sinful past, so there's no chance of senile where-did-it-all-go blues. Well, I'm none of these. Yet fixed by that great face I agreed to go to confession. Not on Saturday afternoon by myself, when I could sneak in one door and out the other. O no! Diabolically

—or divinely, as you will—she had discovered a church that stayed open all night, ostensibly to service actors and such, but actually to catch the subtle change of mood, the lapse of sense in got-away Catholics. Like a twenty-four-hour cafeteria, the Church is ever ready with its ministrations, waiting for the suppressed guilt to rise and bring the sinner to his knees. And sure enough, there in the darkness of this ugly little church was a knot of penitents (from the Latin penis?) preparing themselves in pews that attended the brown-curtained box of forgiveness. When our turn came, Mary preceded me, and stayed but a minute or two. Bless me, Father, for I have sinned, I farted in public and caused others discomfort. My daughter, this is no sin, the others may offer up their discomfort for the suffering souls in purgatory. Well, she popped out and, head bowed, went to the altar to say her penance. I followed, down in darkness I went, onto a felt-covered kneeler, and began. Bless me, Father, for I have sinned. It has been seven years since my last good confession. In that time . . . , and I stopped. I hadn't given a thought to what I would say. Neither had I invented imaginary sins nor recollected real ones. And kneeling there I realized that if I ever intended to confess sincerely it would take enormous preparation. I had been away for seven years, not giving a damn—consciously anyway—and even when you're trying, really doing your best, it's a bitch to stay clean. You have to left-face, right-face, halt, march, doubletime. Let me give you an example. When I was a kid, O twelve or thirteen, I had a compulsion to fashion naughty sayings from the call letters of radio stations. WEAF: Whores Enjoy All Fucking. Great witty truths like that, and each was a mortal sin. So what was I to say now? It was absurd. But this was an old story to the good all-night Father, I guess, because he helped out in my silence. Have you sinned against the sixth commandment, my son? I couldn't remember what the sixth was, but I had faith that like any Catholic cleric he had hit the trouble spot, so I said Yes, Father. Nor was I wrong. The sixth commandment, you Protesting Hebraic free-thinker, is Thou shalt not commit adultery (or do any other dirty thing). He moved right in. Was this sin, or these sins, committed by yourself, with another person, or with an animal? So help me God, that is exactly what he said. By yourself, with another person, or with an animal. Well, two can play this game. All three, Father, I said. He wasn't fazed. Were the sins committed by yourself sins of thought, word, or deed? All, Father. How many times did you commit these sins? Many times, Father. Can you tell me how frequently? Quite frequently, Father. For seven years, he inquired. Yes, Father. How frequently did you commit the sin of deed by yourself? It varied, Father. Once a week, he asked. Yes, Father. More often? Sometimes, Father. Did you commit the sins of word and thought more often than the sins of deed? Yes, Father. How often have you committed sins with another person? Not as often, Father. (Which was putting it mildly.) Did you commit these sins with one person or more than one person? Do you mean at the same time, Father? No, serially. More than one person. Were the other persons of the same sex or the opposite sex? As myself you mean, Father? Yes. (Why should I discriminate, I thought.) Both, Father. Did you commit these sins more often with persons of the opposite sex or with persons of the same sex? (Here I thought I'd draw the line.) Opposite, Father. And have you sinned with animals? (Jesus, what a dirty mind!) Yes, Father. Very often? No, Father. Have you committed mortal sins against any of the other commandments? Yes, Father. Which commandments? I was silent, I didn't know the goddamned numbers. But again he helped right out. Have you stolen? Yes, Father. A large amount? I paused, thinking of the complications, but what the hell! Yes, Father. More than a hundred dollars? Yes, Father. More than five hundred? Yes, Father. How much did you steal? Fifty thousand dollars, Father. Have you made restitution? No, Father. You must make restitution if you are to be forgiven, do you understand that? Yes, Father. Do you still have the money? Yes, Father. Do you intend to return it? Yes, Father. You must do this, if it is in your power. I understand, Father. Are you under suspicion for this crime? No, Father, I don't believe so. It is not necessary that you confess to the authorities, returning the stolen money is sufficient. Yes, Father, thank you. There was a mutual silence. I think he was afraid to go on. Finally, though, Have you committed any other serious sins? Yes, Father. Have you injured anyone? That isn't it, Father. You must tell me what it is, if you are to receive absolution. It's a very bad sin, Father. There is no sin beyond absolution if the sinner is repentant, what is the sin, my son? I'm ashamed to tell it, Father. You must, otherwise you cannot be absolved, do you understand that? Yes, Father, but I don't think this sin can be absolved. To believe that is a sin in itself, my son, God's mercy is infinitely large. Well then, Father, I said, I have . . . lied in confession. And I broke out into nervous laughter, and I couldn't stop, so I beat it, nearly taking the curtain down as I went. Luckily Mary was waiting outside on the church steps. But talk about orgone boxes! The Pure Food and Drug people ought to get hot on confessionals, that's what I say. Anyway, she was suffused with happiness, certain that I must feel reborn. Quickly I got her away from the church, I was afraid somehow that the priest would come tailing after us. He didn't, of course. Did you say your penance, she asked. Well, I explained, the penance will take a little doing. She nodded understandingly, and we went off for a few drinks. Now we are engaged, really engaged, she said. But I had lost my taste for Mary. I took her home finally and kissed her lightly on the cheek and decided she was not for me.

JOHN RECHY

Miss Destiny: The Fabulous Wedding

1

The first time I saw Miss Destiny was of course in Pershing Square, on the cool, almost cold, moist evening of a warm smoggy day.

Im sitting in the park with Chuck the cowboy on the railing facing 5th Street. "Oh oh, here comes Miss Destinee," says Chuck, a cowboy youngman with widehat and boots, very slim of course, of course very slow, with sideburns of course almost to his chin, and a giant tattoo on his arm that says: DEATH BEFORE DISHONOR. "Destinee's last husband jes got busted pushing hard stuff, man," Chuck is going on, "an she is hot for a new one, so watch out, man—but if you ain got a pad, you can always make it at Destinee's—it's like a gone mission, man!"

Indeed, indeed! here comes Miss Destiny! fluttering out of the shadows into the dimlights along the ledges like a giant firefly—flirting, calling out to everyone: "Hello, darling, I love you—I love you too, dear—so very much—ummmm!" Kisses flung recklessly into the wind. . . . "What oh what did Chuck say to you, darling?" to me, coming on breathlessly rushing words. "You must understand right here and now that Chuck still loves me, like all my exhusbands (youre new in town, dear, or I would certainly have seen you before, and do you have a place to stay?—I live on Spring Street and there is a 'Welcome!' mat at the door)—oh, they

nevuh! can forget me—of course I loved Chuck once too—"
(sigh) "—such a butch cowboy, look at him—but havent I
loved every new hustler in town?—but oh this restlessness
in me!—and are you married, dear?—oh, the lady doth indeed protest Too Much—" (this last addressed to Jenny Lu,
still bumping (woe-*uh!*). I *adore* Married men—as long as
they are Faithful to me, you understand, of course—and I
must warn you right here and now about Pauline, who is
the most evil people in this city and you must stay away
from her when she tries to make out with all kinds of—
Ah Beg To Tell You—" ("Whewoo!" sighed Chuck.) "—untrue promises as some—people—have—found—out—" looking coldly at Chuck, then rushing on: "Oh I am, as everyone will tell you, A Very Restless Woman—"

She—he (Miss Destiny is a man)—went on about her—his
—restlessness, her husbands, asking me questions in between,
figuring out how Bad I was ("Have you been 'interviewed'
yet by Miss Lorelei?—I mean Officer Morgan, dear—we call
her Miss Lorelei. And dont let her scare you, dear—and
Im sure you wont—why, Miss Lorelei—I mean, Sergeant
Morgan—is as much a lady as I am: I saw her in the mens-
room one time, and she ran everybody out—except this cute
young boy—and— . . .")—looking alternately coyly and coldly at Chuck then me seductively: all of which you will recog-
nize as the queen's technique to make you feel like such an
irresistible so masculine so sexual so swinging stud, and
queens can do it better than most real girls, queens being
Uninhibited.

Now Miss Destiny is a youngman possibly 20 but quite
as possibly 18 and very probably 25, with false I.D. like
everyone else if she is underage: a slim young queen with
masses and masses of curly red hair (which she fondly calls
her "rair"), oh, and it tumbles gaily over a pale skinny face
almost smothering it at times. Unpredictably occasionally
she comes on with crazy Southern sounds cultivated, you
will learn, all the way from northern Pennsylvania.

"Oh my dear!" she exclaims now, fluffing out her "rair,"
"here I am talking all about my Sex life, and we have not
been Properly Introduced! . . . Im Miss Destiny, dear—and
let me hasten to tell you before you hear it wrong from
othuh sources that I am famous even in Los gay Angeles—
why, I went to this straight party in High Drag (and I

mean *High,* honey—gown, stockings, ostrich plumes in my flaming rair), and—"

"An you know who she was dancing with?" Chuck interrupted.

"The Vice, my dear," Miss Destiny said flatly, glowering at Chuck.

"An she was busted, man—for ah mas—mask— . . ."

"Masquerading, dear. . . . But how was I to know the repressed queer was the vice squad—tell me? . . ." And she goes on breathlessly conjuring up the Extravagant Scene. . . .

(*Oh shes dancing like Cinderella at the magic ball in this Other World shes longingly invading, and her prince-charming turns out to be: the vice squad. And oh Miss Destiny gathers her skirts and tries to run like in the fairytale, but the vice grabs her roughly and off she goes in a very real coach to the glasshouse, the feathers trembling now nervously. Miss Destiny insists she is a real woman leave her alone. (But oh, oh! how can she hide That Thing between his legs which should belong there only when it is somebody else's?) . . . All lonesome tears and Humiliation, Miss Destiny ends up in the sex tank: a wayward Cinderella. . . .*)

"Now, honey," she says with real indignation, "I can see them bustin me for Impersonating a man—but a woman!—*really*! . . ." And you will notice that Miss Destiny like all the other swinging queens in the world considers herself every bit a Lady. "But nevuh mind," she went on, "I learned things in the countyfawm I didnt know before—like how to make eyeshadow out of spit and bluejeans—and oh my dear the kites I flew!—I mean to say, no one can say I didnt send my share of invitations out! . . . Of course, I *do* have to go regularly to the county psychiatrist (thats a mind doctor, dears)—to be (would you believe it? this is what they actually told me:) 'cured'! Well! One more session with him, and I'll have *him* on the couch!—but now—" turning her attention to me fullblast, because, you will understand, Miss Destiny scouts at night among the drifting youngmen, and at the same time you can tell shes out to bug Chuck: and when she asked me would I go to the flix with her now ("across the street, where it is Divine but you mustnt be seen there too often," she explains, "because they will think youre free trade— . . ."), Chuck said: "It

would not do you no good, Destinee, they will not let you
in the men's head."

"*Miss* Destiny, *Mister* Chuck," she corrects him airily.

And went on: "Didnt I tell you all my exhusbands are
jealous of me? Chuck lived with me, dear," she explains,
"as just about every other studhustler has at one time or
another, I must add modestly. But, baby, it was a turbulent
marriage (that means very stormy, dear). Why, I just
couldnt drag Chuck from the window—he—"

"Oh, man," interrupts Chuck. "Next to Miss Destinee's
pad theres this real swell cunt an she walks aroun all day
in her brassiere—standin by the window, an she—"

"But I fixed that!" Miss Destiny says triumphantly. "I
nailed the damn windowshades so no one can look out at
that cunt anymore! . . . Oh!" she sighed, her hand at her
forehead, "those days were trying days. Chuck's a good
hustler—but hes too lazy even to try to score sometimes.
And, honey, my unemployment check went just so far:
You see, I took a job just long enough to qualify for unemployment, and then I turned up all madeup and they let
me go—and everytime they call me up for a job, why I
turn up in drag and they wont have me! . . . But anyway— . . ."

Looking at Chuck and Miss Destiny—as she rushes on
now about the Turbulent Times—I know the scene: Chuck
the masculine cowboy and Miss Destiny the femme queen:
making it from day to park to bar to day like all the others
in that ratty world of downtown L.A. which I will make
my own: the world of queens and malehustlers and what
they thrive on, the queens being technically men but no one
thinks of them that way—always "she"—their "husbands"
being the masculine vagrants—fleetingly and often out of
convenience sharing the queens' pads—never considering
theyre involved with another man (the queen), and as long
as the hustler goes only with queens—and with other men
only for scoring (which is making or taking sexmoney, getting a meal, making a pad)—he is himself not considered
"queer"—he remains, in the vocabulary of that world,
"trade."

"Yes," Miss Destiny is going on, "those were stormy times
with Chuck—and then, being from cowcountry, God bless
him, Chuck believes every Big story: like when Pauline
told him she'd really set him up—"

"Man," Chuck explained, laughing, "Pauline is this queen thats got more bull than Texas!"

"Can you imagine?" Miss Destiny says to me. "She offered him a Cadillac! Pauline! Who hasnt even got enough to keep her dragclothes in proper shape! . . . But nevuhmind, let him be gullible (thats someone who believes untrue stories). And, besides," she says with a toss of her head, "I flipped over Sandy, a bad new stud. . . . But Chuck's still jealous of me—he knows Im looking for a new husband— now that poor Sandy (my most recent ex, dear) got busted, and I know he didnt have any hard narcotics on him like they say he did—they planted them in his car— . . . Shake that moneymakuh, honey!—" (this to a spadequeen swishing by) "—and I still love my Sandy—did the best I could, tried to bail him out, hire a good attuhnee, but it was no good—they laughed when I said he was my husband. The quality of muhcee is mighty strained indeed—as the dear Portia said (from Shakespeare, my dears—a very Great writer who wrote ladies' roles for dragqueens in his time). And it breaks my heart to think of my poor Sandy in the joint away from women all that time, him so redhot he might turn queer, but oh no not my Sandy, hes all stud. If I know him, he'll come out of the joint rich, hustling the guards. . . . And I tried to be faithful—but the years will be so long—and what can a girl do, and restless the way I am?—restless and crying muhself to sleep night aftuh night, missing him—missing him. But my dears, I realize I Will Have To Go On—he would want it that way. Well, queens have died eaten by the ah worm of ah love, as the Lovely Cleopatra said—she was The Queen of Ancient Egypt—" (quoting, misquoting Shakespeare—saying it was a lovely he-roine who said it in the play—taking it for granted—a safe assumption in her world—that no one will understand her anyway). "Then Miss Thing said to me (Miss Thing is a fairy perched on my back like some people have a monkey or a conscience)," she· explained, "well, Miss Thing said to me, 'Miss Destiny dear, dont be a fool, fix your lovely rair and find you a new husband—make it per- manent this time by really getting Married—and even if you have to stretch your unemployment, dont allow him to push or hustle' (which breaks up a marriage)—and Miss Thing said, 'Miss Destiny dear, have a real wedding this time.' . . . A real wedding," Miss Destiny sighed wistfully,

"Like every young girl should have at least once. . . . And
when it happens oh it will be the most simpuhlee Fabulous
wedding the Westcoast has evuh seen! with oh the most
beautiful queens as bridesmaids! and the handsomest studs
as ushers! (and you will absolutely have to remove those
boots, Chuck)—and *Me!* . . . Me . . . in virginwhite . . .
coming down a winding staircase . . . carrying a white bou-
quet! . . . and my family will be crying for joy. . . . And there
will be champagne! cake! a real priest to puhfawn the Ceremony!—" She broke off abruptly, shutting her eyes delir-
iously as if to visualize the scene better. Then she opened
them again, onto the frantic teeming world of Pershing
Square. . . .

"They will bust you again for sure if you have that
wedding, Miss Destinee," said Chuck gravely.

"It would be worth it," sighed Miss Destiny. "Oh, it would
be worth it."

Then we noticed a welldressed man standing a few feet
from us in the shadows, staring at us intently until he saw
us looking back and he shifted his gaze, began to smoke,
looked up furtively again.

Miss Destiny smiled brightly at him, but he didnt smile
back at her, and Miss Destiny said obviously he is a queer
and so he must want a man. "So darlings, I will leave you
to him and him to whomevuh eenie-meenie-miney he wants.
But let me tell you, my dear—" me—confidentially "—that
when they dress that elegantly around here, why, they will
make all kinds of promises and give you oh two bucks,"
and Chuck said oh no the score was worth at least twenty,
and Miss Destiny laughs like Tallulah Bankhead, who is
the Idol of all queens, and says in a husky voice, "Dalling,
this is not your young inexperienced sistuh you are talkin
to, this is your mothuh, who has been a-round. . . . Why,
Miss Thing told me about this sweet stud kid going for a
dollar!— . . . Ah, well, as my beloved sweet Juliet said,
Parting is: such—sweet—sorrow— . . ." And she sighed now,
being Juliet, then whispered to me loud enough for Chuck
to hear, "There will be other times, my dear—when you
are not Working."

And she moved away with peals of queenly laughter,
flirting again, fluttering again, flamboyantly swishing, just as
she had come on, saying hello to everyone: "Good evening,
Miss Saint Moses, dear— . . ." spreading love, throwing

kisses, bringing her delicate hands to her face, sighing, "Too Much!" after some goodlooking youngman she digs, glancing back at Chuck and me as the man moved out of the shadows, closer to us, jingling money.

So there goes Miss Destiny leaving Pershing Square, all gayety, all happiness, all laughter.

"I love you too, dear, ummmm, so much. . . ."

2

Those first days in Los Angeles, I was newly dazzled by the world into which my compulsive journey through submerged lives had led me—newly hypnotized by the life of the streets.

I had rented a room in a hotel on Hope Street—on the fringes of that world but still outside of it (in order always to have a place where I could be completely alone when I must be). Thus the duality of my existence was marked by a definite boundary: Pershing Square: east of there when the desire to be with people churned within me; west of there to the hotel when I had to be alone. . . . At times, after having combed the bars, the streets, the park, I would flee as if for protection to that hotel room.

Yet other times I needed people fiercely—needed the anarchy of the streets. . . .

And Main Street in Los Angeles is such an anarchy.

This is clip street, hustle street—frenzied-nightactivity street: the moving back and forth against the walls; smoking, peering anxiously to spot the bulls before they spot you; the rushing in and out of Wally's and Harry's: long crowded malehustling bars.

And here too are the fairyqueens—the queens from Everywhere, America—the queenly exiles looking for new "husbands" restlessly among the vagrant hustlers with no place to stay, and the hustlers will often clip the queens (if there is anything to clip), and the queens will go on looking for their own legendary permanent "Daddies" among the older men who dig the queens' special brand of gone sexplay, seldom finding those permanent connections, and living in Main and Spring Street holes: sometimes making it (employed and unemployed, taking their daddies and being taken by the hustlers)—sometimes hardly, sometimes not at all.

And the malehustlers live with them off and on, making

it from bar to lonesome room, bragging about the $50 score with the fruit from Bel Air who has two swimming pools, jack, and said he'd see you again (but if he didnt show, you dont say that), and youre clinching a dime and a nickel for draft beer at Wally's or Harry's or the 1-2-3 or Ji-Ji's so you can go inside and score early, and make it with one of the vagrant young girls to prove to yourself youre still All Right.

And so Main Street is an anarchy where the only rule is Make It! . . . And the only reminders of the world beyond its boundaries are the policewagons that cruise the streets —the cops that pick you at random out of Hooper's all-night coffee shop after 2:00 in the morning. . . . The free jammed ride to the glasshouse for fingerprints . . .

Rock-n-roll sounds fill the rancid air.

This was the world I joined.

A couple of blocks away from Main Street, on Spring— squashed on either side by gray apartment buildings (*walls greasy from days of cheap cooking, cobwebbed lightbulbs feebly hiding in opaque darkness, windowscreens if any smooth as velvet with grime—where queens and hustlers and other exiles hibernate*)—just beyond the hobo cafeteria where panhandlers hang dismally outside in the cruel neonlight (*fugitives from the owlfaces of the Salvation Army fighting Evil with no help from God or the cops; fugitives from Uplifting missionwords and lambstew*)—is the 1-2-3.

Outside, a cluster of pushers gather like nervous caged monkeys, openly offering pills and maryjane thrills, and you see them scurrying antlike to consult with Dad-o, the Negro king of downtown smalltime pushers—and Dad-o, sitting royally at the bar like a heap of very black shiny dough, says yes or no arbitrarily.

And that is the way it is.

I saw Miss Destiny again one Saturday night at the 1-2-3. And that is when it swings.

"Oooee . . ." she squealed. "I *wondered* where you were, baby, and I have thought about you—and thought, why hes gone already—*Escaped!*—and oh Im so glad youre not, and come here, I want you to meet my dear sistuhs and their boyfriends—" being, naturally, the downtown queens and hustlers who are Miss Destiny's friends.

And squeezing expertly through the thick crowd, Miss Destiny led me into a cavern of trapped exiles—of painted sallow-faced youngmen, artificial manikin faces like masks; of tough-looking masculine hustlers, young fugitives from everywhere and everything, young lean faces already proclaiming Doom; of jaded old and middle-aged men seeking the former and all-aged homosexuals seeking the latter—all crowded into this long narrow, ugly bar, plaster crumbling in chunks as if it had gnawed its own way into the wall; long benches behind the tables, splintered, decaying; mirrors streaked yellow—a bar without visible windows; cigarette smoke tinged occasionally with the unmistakable odor of maryjane hovering over us almost unmoving like an ominous hand. . . . And the faces emerge from the thick smoke like in those dark moody photographs which give you the feeling that the subjects have been imprisoned by the camera.

"This is Trudi," Miss Destiny was saying, and Trudi is probably the realest and sweetest-looking queen in L.A., and youd have to be completely queer not to dig her. Her hair is long enough for a woman, short enough for a man. Her eyelashes were painted arched over round blue coquettish eyes, and of all the queens I will meet in L.A., Trudi has most accurately been able to duplicate the female stance so that, unlike most other queens, she has not become the mere parody of a woman. "Hi, baby," she says, pursing her lips cutely, "welcome to the snakepit." She indicates the scene about her as if she had been born to reign over it.

"And this is Skipper," Miss Destiny continues, and as if presenting his credentials adds, in a lower tone for me only —and I can barely hear her over the blasting music: "He used to be a physique model, baby, and he became quite famous in Hollywood once—hes even hustled Officer Morgan—and that's the truth—but he'll tell you all about that, Im sure—" And Skipper is restlessly scrutinizing the familiar scene; almost—it seems at times—in bewilderment— as if looking around him each moment, he is newly aware of where he is. Often he squinted as if to cloud the scene from his mind. He is now—and it will turn out is usually —talking about a plan to hit the Bigtime again. "Hi, jack!" he says, and his eyes rake the bar. . . . And all at once he doesnt look nearly as young as he first appeared.

"And my dear, Dear sistuh Lola—" Miss Destiny is saying (queens calling each other sisters); and Lola is quite

possibly "dear, Dear" because undoubtedly shes the ugliest
queen in the world, with painted eyes like a silent moviestar, and a black turtleneck sweater running into her coarse
shiny black hair so that it seems shes wearing a hood—and
has a husky meanman's voice and looks like nothing but an
ugly man in semidrag. "Always room for one more," she
rasps, welcoming me.

"And you have of course already met Mistuh Chuck,"
Miss Destiny says sighingly, and Chuck tipped his widehat
in salutation: "Howdee."

"And this is Tiguh—" Miss Destiny went on. And Tiger
(names, you will notice, as obviously emphatically masculine
as the queens' are emphatically obviously feminine and for
the same reason: to emphasize the roles they will play) is a
heavily tattooed youngman who has precisely that quality
you sense in caged tigers glowering savagely through iron
bars.

"And Darling Dolly—" Miss Destiny said.

And Darling Dolly corrects Miss Destiny: "Darling Dolly
Dane, Destiny dear."

And Destiny corrects her: "*Miss* Destiny, Darling Dolly
Dane, dear."

Truly, you will admit, Darling Dolly Dane is cute in the
dimlight and smokeshadows, with softlooking creamskin and
dancing eyes and a loose sweater tonight and slacks—acting
like a flirt teenage girl out to get laid.

"And Buddy—" Miss Destiny finishes with the introduc-
tions.

Buddy is a blond very young boy, I would say 19—at
whom, as Miss Destiny and I sit at the already-crowded
table, Darling Dolly Dane is glaring. Miss Destiny tells me
confidentially, to explain the cool looks between Darling Dolly
and Buddy, that Buddy had been living with Darling Dolly
Dane until last night when she found he hocked some of
her drag clothes and she locked him out and he had to
sleep in his brokendown Mercury, which may not even be
his. . . .

Now a score at the bar is ostentatiously turning us on
to free drinks—and cokes for Darling Dolly, who is making
such a thing about her Not Drinking. On a small balcony
over the head, the rock-n-roll spades are going, perched
like a nest of restless blackbirds. A queen, obviously drunk,
has climbed on it and has started to do an imitation strip,

and Ada, who runs the bar and is a real woman—a mean, tough blonde like a movie madam—climbs after her dragging her roughly off the balcony just as the queen is unsnapping her imaginary brassiere, saying:

"Sssssssssssssufferrrrrrrrrrr. . . ."

At the table, everyone is talking, eyes constantly searching the bar. The beat of the music somehow matches the movements, the stares, the muted desperation all around; the smothered moans of the spade now blaring words from the balcony is like a composite moan, a wail emanating in unison from everyone crushed into this dirty bar. . . . Darling Dolly is breathlessly explaining the Severe Jolt she got when she got home and found her best drag clothes gone: "My lovely lace negligee—my studded shoes!" Buddy shakes his head and says to the table: "I needed the bread." Darling Dolly stabs him with a look. Chuck says hes heard of a malehouse in Hollywood where he can make hundreds of dollars a day: "But I don know where it is so I cain apply." Miss Destiny says, "Chuck, my dear, you are just too lazy to get ahead—remember the $15 score I got you and you fell asleep?" . . . Trudi is wondering wheres her daddy, and Miss Destiny explains to me that Trudi's "daddy" is an old man whos been "keeping Trudi for ages—and keeps Skipper, too, sometimes—but indirectly": Skipper living off and on with Trudi and hitting it big occasionally—"after being Really Big in Hollywood once"—and going away, coming back to Trudi's. . . . Nearby, an emaciated man with devouring deep-buried eyes is pretending to read the titles on the jukebox, but it's obvious that he is fascinatedly studying Tiger's tattoos—and Tiger, noticing this, glances at him with huge undisguised contempt, which sends the emaciated man into an ecstasy of sick smiles.

Now the queens at the table are wondering aloud who the score buying the juice is digging: the queens or otherwise, and which one. And which does it turn out hes digging? The queens. And which one? Darling Dolly Dane. And when this became known, by means of the "waitress," Darling Dolly skips over to him, perches on the stool next to him at the bar, and says, "Another tall cool Coca-Cola please, honey, and make it straight." Miss Destiny sighed, "Well, lordee, Tara is saved tonight."

Immediately Skipper had a plan to clip the score, and Trudi says philosophically, "Dont get nervous, youll shake

the beads"—(the beads being life—fate—chance—anything)
—"and besides, Darling Dolly saw him first." Miss Destiny
says theyre all Too Much. Suddenly shes becoming depressed
—and the obvious reason is that the score who it turned out
dug queens didnt dig her.

"Oh, Im *really* depressed now!" Miss Destiny said. Someone had mentioned that Pauline had just walked in. I looked,
and theres Pauline—a heavily painted queen who thinks
she looks like Sophia Loren—with a collar like the wicked
queen's in Snow White.

Miss Destiny said icily: "Pauline . . . is a lowlife . . .
prostitute."

Trudi: "A cheap whore."

Lola, in her husky man's voice and glowering nearsighted-
ly: "A slut."

Trudi: "A common streetwalker."

Lola: "A chippy."

Miss Destiny—conclusively, viciously: "A *cocksucker!*"

Chuck gagged on his beer. "She ain got nothin on you,
Destinee!"

Then quickly, diverting attention from Pauline and putting
Chuck down with a look, Miss Destiny asked me abruptly
do I know anyone in Hollywood who has a beautiful home
with a beautiful Winding Staircase where she can come
down—"to marry," she explains, "my new husband and
spend my life blissfully (thats very happily, dear) on unemployment with him forever."

Darling Dolly Dane returned suddenly very angrily lisping
the man had offered her two bucks, after such a show of
buying drinks. "And do you know what the sonuvabitch
wants for two miserable goddam bucks?"

"To marry you," said Destiny aloofly.

Skipper had a plan to clip the score.

"I dont have my husband picked out yet," Miss Destiny
went on as if there had been no interruption. "That part
isnt too important yet—I'll wait until I fall in love again
(dont look at Pauline, shes looking over here)—the important
thing now is the Winding Staircase."

Darling Dolly Dane: "Two miserable bucks!"

Lola: "Youve gone for less, dear."

Darling Dolly Dane, wiggling: "This aint no change-ma-
chine, Mae."

Chuck: "Hey, sweetie, you light up with a nickel?"

Skipper: "Darling Dolly, you go with the cholly, and I'll cool it by the parking lot—"

Tiger: "Stomp the shit out of him."

Trudi, sighing as if no one but she really understands: "My dears, I tell you it's the goddam beads."

Buddy: "Darling Dolly, tell him *ten* so you can get your drag clothes out of hock."

Miss Destiny sighs: "Oh! this! is! too! depressing!—really, my dears, you talk like common thieves and muggers—and what am I doing here? . . . Now as I was saying—what?— oh, yes— . . ."

Now the score—checking the looks and mean sounds— starts to leave, and Darling Dolly rushes after him, leaving Skipper plotting, and she whispers something to the score (on tiptoes; she is very short), and as they went out together, Buddy laughs and laughs: "Two bucks!" And Lola said, "Youve gone for less, dear."

I promised Destiny to tell her if I met anyone with a beautiful home and a winding staircase.

"Baby," she said abruptly, unexpectedly moodily, "dont you think I look *real?*" And before anyone can answer, possibly afraid of the answer, she went on hurriedly, "Oh, but you should have seen me when I first came out."

"Here it comes, dears, the goddam Miss Destiny beads," said Trudi, recognizing Miss Destiny's cue and looking over the crowd for her "daddy," who is to meet her here tonight and take her—she says—to Chasen's—Beverly Hills' exclusive restaurant.

And indeed, just like that, Miss Destiny—on—has begun to tell me about when she first came out and how she became Miss Destiny. Soon, Im the only one listening to her, the others moving away restlessly, having heard it or portions of it or a version of it: Trudi finds her "daddy"—a fat middle-aged man—and Chuck goes to the bar and is now talking to a flashily dressed fruit in a redcheckered vest. Skipper is playing the shuffleboard, ramming the disk vengefully into the pins. . . . Wordlessly entranced, the emaciated man is standing next to Tiger where hes leaning against the peeling wall. Buddy has left the bar, probably going to Main Street or the park. And Lola is sitting alone at the bar, elbows propping her ugly face dejectedly. Looking at her from the distance, I realized how much she looks like a lesbian.

"Before I flipped," Miss Destiny was saying, rushing, as if the hurried flow of her words would keep me with her, "I was very Innocent," and I could sense the huge depression suddenly, perhaps that one rejection just now echoing into the very depths of her consciousness setting off a thousand other rejections. "Of course," she went on, "Miss Thing had told me, 'Why how ridiculous!—that petuh between your legs simpuhlee does not belong, dear.' And oh, once, when I was a kid, I asked my father for *paperdolls*, and he brought me some Superman *comicbooks* instead—and then, oh! I asked him for *Superman* paperdolls. . . . And they were always so ashamed of me when I wanted to dress up —and my father threw me out—on a cold night, too—and I took my doll with me that I slept with since I was little —and I had to quit college (where I studied Dramatics, dear, but not for long, because they wouldnt let me play the girl's part), and I went to Philadelphia. And the first thing I did, why, I bought myself a flaming-red dress and highheeled sequined shoes and everyone thought I was Real, and Miss Thing said, 'Hurray, honey! youve done it—stick to it,' and I met a rich daddy, who thought I was Real, and he flipped over me and took me to a straight cocktail party. . . ."

And so, with Eminent contradictions (I must warn you), the wayward saga of Miss Destiny unfolds—that night at the 1-2-3, in the ocean of searching faces:

"Naturally," she continued, "I got into the Finest circles. Philadelphia society and all that—and Im sippin muh cocktail at this party when in walks the most positively gorgeous youngman I have evuh seen. And he stares at me! Walked away from the hostess—who was a real lady (a society model, baby, and later she became a Moviestar and married that king—you know)—" muttering bitch after Pauline who just then passed brushing my shoulder purposely to bug Miss Destiny "—and this gorgeous youngman, why, he comes to me and says—just like that—'You Are My Destiny!' and I thought he said, 'You are *Miss* Destiny,' mistaking me you know for some other girl, and when the hostess says Im the most beautiful fish shes evuh seen, what is my name, Im terrified the gorgeous youngman will drop me if Im not who I think he thinks I am, so I say, 'I am *Miss* Destiny,' and *he* thinks I said, 'I am *his* destiny'

(he told me later), and he says, 'Yes oh yes she is,' and
from then on I am Miss Destiny—"

*(Oh they go home that night and Miss Destiny must
confess she is not a real woman, but, oh, oh, he doesnt
care, having of course flipped over her, and he takes her to
his country estate, his family naturally being Fabulously
rich, and they simply Idolize Miss Destiny. . . .)*

"His name was Duke," Miss Destiny sighed, "and when I
met him, oh I remember, they were playing *La Varsouviana*
(thats 'Put Your Little Foot,' dear)—you see, although it
was a cocktail party, it was so Elegant that they had an
orchestra—and how I loved him, and I know thats a strange
name—Duke—but it was his real name, not a nickname—
but he would be a wild rose by any other name and smell as
sweet! . . . Being aristocrats, all his family had strange
names: his mother's name was ah Alexandria, just like the
ah queen of ah ancient Sparta who killed the ah emperor in
Greek mythology (those are very old stories, dear)—"

Suddenly here is Darling Dolly Dane back gasping tug-
ging at Miss Destiny, who of course resents the intrusion
in the middle of her autobiography. "Destiny, Destiny,
quick," Darling Dolly pleads, "Ive got to have the key to
your pad right away quick hurry!" I notice Darling Dolly is
carrying a small bundle that looks suspiciously like a pair
of pants. All right, all right—and what does Darling Dolly
want the key for? Darling Dolly Dane says she just clipped
the score she went with who promised her the deuce, remember? She told him dont bother getting a room, give the
extra bread to her, honey, and: "I know a swinging head in
an apartment house right around here," Darling Dolly told
the score, who was pretty juiced anyhow. So they go up to
the head, and the score is thinking this is really getting
Saturday-night kicks: gone sex! with a cute queen! in a head!
And she took off his pants cooing and his shorts cooing and
ran out with both pants and shorts—and wallet. "And look!"
she said now, pulling out the wallet, which was green, green
like a tree. "So Ive got to go to your pad in case he comes
back looking for me." "Without pants?" Destiny asked, and
adds: "And why my pad? why not yours?" Darling Dolly
explains it's too far and too early. Miss Destiny tilted her
head, consulting her gay fairy. "Miss Thing says dont give
you the key," Miss Destiny said, "but then Miss Thing aint

nevuh been busted—so here—" Darling Dolly dashed out with the key. Miss Destiny sighed Darling Dolly was positively Too Much, and I noticed Chuck going out, widehat over his eyes, with the flashy fruit. . . . Lola is still sitting very much alone glowering at her madeup face in the mirror behind the bar. . . .

And Miss Destiny continues typically as if nothing had interrupted her story:

"And then, before I knew it, Duke was dead. . . . He was a truckdriver, and sometimes we were so poor we couldnt even make it: I had to hustle in drag in order to keep us going—of course, he didnt know this—" And then remembering The Wealth and the country estate: "Well, you see his family disinherited him, they couldnt *stand* me." And then remembering the way his family Idolized her: "Well, you see they *loved* me at first, until they Found Out—"

(Now Duke the Aristocrat is Duke the Truckdriver, disinherited but oh so in love with Miss Destiny, and on a cold murky damp foggy day his truck turns over on the highway, the brakes screech shrilly, the wheels are turning round, round, round. . . . The sirens wail: Eeeeeeeeeeeeeeeeeeeeeeeeeeeee-uh. And When They Came To Tell Miss Destiny, she senses it before they say anything and says: I Want To Be Alone . . . and there is no one to turn to. . . .)

"You see I was an orphan," and then remembering her father who threw her out: "I had lived with my aunt and uncle and called them my father and mother—and it was my uncle who threw me out, the same uncle who Raped me when I was eight years old and I screamed it hurt so and my aunt said forget it, it would go away (she was a degenerate). . . . And each time I close my eyes, I see those goddam wheels going round, round, round—and I hear that tune they were playing when I met him. ('Put your little foot')," she hummed. . . . "And it wont stop until I hear the *crash! . . . Oh!*"

(So Miss Destiny lones it to Washington D.C. where she makes it with men who think shes Real. And when they reach That Point in the cramped car she must insist on, she will say no honey not that, I have got the rag on—she will of course be welltaped. "But thats no reason why we cant have a swinging time anyway." And if not she will say shes underage and threaten to scream rape. (And dont ask how,

*Or If, she always got away with it.) But a jealous bar-
tender, who Knows, tells three sailors who want to make it
with her that shes not a fish, shes a fruit, and the sailorboys
wait outside for her, mean, and start to tear off her beautiful dress and say, If youre a girl wow the world is yours
honey, but if youre a goddam queer start praying. . . . And
oh Miss Destiny runs as you will begin to think she is always doing, and they grab her roughly as you will begin to
think they are always doing, and she rushes into the street
and into a taxi passing by luckily and the driver says have
you been clipped or raped lady?—and: I will take you to
the heat station. She says oh no please forget it . . . and
goes back to Philadelphia to place a Wreath on Duke's
grave, and comes to Los Angeles with a Southern Ac-
cent. . . .)*

"And I became what you see now: a wild restless woman
with countless of exhusbands," Miss Destiny said. "But do
you know, baby, that I have never been Really Married? I
mean in White, coming down a Winding Staircase. . . . And
I *will!* I will fall in love again soon—I can feel it—and
when I do, I will have my Fabulous Wedding, in a pearl-
white gown—" and she went on delightedly until she
caught sight of Pauline's reflection in the panel of mirrors
behind the bar, and something about the way Pauline was
looking in our direction clearly threatened she would come
right over and introduce herself and bug Miss Destiny.

"Goddam queer," Miss Destiny murmured, and she was
fiercely depressed.

3

I left the 1-2-3 and went to Ji-Ji's bar—another malehustling and queen bar: but tougher. You walk under a
small tattered awning into a dark cavelike room. Beyond the
dark, through a tunnel-like opening, the bar leads into a
small narrow lunchcounter, where malehustlers and queens
sit eating. And Ji-Ji, the old, haggard queen who owns this
bar, reigns over it adoringly as if it were a wayward mission—a hidden underground sheltering those rebels from
the life that spat her out. . . . Dad-o, the Negro pusher, is
here now, huddled at one end of the bar, almost eaten up
by the darkness, except where the light from under the bar
gleams in shiny eery highlights on his sweaty skin; hes

talking to a skinny boy next to him—obviously a pusher.

It is much more quiet here than at the 1-2-3—the superficial gayety is absent, there is a brooding silence: an undisguised purposefulness to make it. Even the scores who haunt Ji-Ji's are colder. They stand appraising the young malehustlers as if they were up for auction.

As I walked in, a tall newyorkdressed man leans toward me and murmurs: "Lets get out of here and go to my place, boy—I got a bar there myself." His assurance bugs me strangely. The guilt seizes me powerfully. I feel an overwhelming shame suddenly for looking so easily available. "Youre taking a lot for granted," I said. He shrugs his shoulders. "It's Ji-Ji's, isnt it?" he says—but—not so sure of himself any more—he walks away hurriedly. . . . I leave the bar immediately, the sudden inexplicable shame scorching me inside. The youngman who had been with Dad-o is now outside. The night is brighter than the bar. . . . The youngman asks me furtively if I want to turn on. He opens his hand, tiny joints of marijuana squirm in his palm. He looks strangely like a biblical prophet—with a beard, infinitely sorrowful eyes. I say no.

When I came back to the 1-2-3, Chuck was back too. He asked me to go outside with him. "I got some sticks," he says, "you wanna blast?" (I remember the prophet-faced youngman only moments earlier.) . . . I walk with Chuck along Spring Street, left, across Broadway, then Hill, beyond the tunnel, around the area with all the trees. Chuck says: "I don really dig this stuff, man—too much of a hassle to hold any, an I don dig hasslin it noway—but somebody turned me on free—so might jes as well. . . ." We squatted there among the shadows, shut in by the trees, smoking like Indians—or maybe, more like children forbiddenly in a garage.

We went to Main Street, and Im feeling an intensified sense of perception—as if suddenly I can see clearly. Now Main Street is writhing with the frantic nothing-activity in the late hours. We walked into Wally's, exploding with smoke. Then to Harry's bar and more smoke, more streaky mirrors, more hungry eyes and stares—and later, before the burlesque house with the winking lights and the pictures of nude women, we saw three girls, and Chuck went casually and talked to them and they said yes. They belonged obviously to that breed of young girls with whom the hustlers periodically prove their masculinity. Like the malehustlers, they live the best they can from day to day. . . . We went back to the 1-2-3 to look for Skipper or Buddy to come along with us. Miss Destiny was standing outside with Lola, and when she saw the girls with us, she stomped angrily inside the bar. We found Skipper, and we got into Buddy's car and Skipper made it run, and since no one had a place to go, we drove to Echo Park.

And the night was miraculously clear as it rarely is in Los Angeles, and the moon hung sadly in the sky as unconcerned as the world, as we sexhuddled in the car with the three lost girls. . . .

We left the girls at Silverlake and came back to the 1-2-3, where Miss Destiny, skyhigh, rushed at us shrieking, "You know whats the crazy matter with you, all of you? youre so dam gone on your own damselves you have to hang around queens to prove youre such fine dam studs, and the first dam cunt that shows, you go lapping after her like hot dam dawgs!" Then she cooled off right away and said drive her to Bixel Street, where someone (shes playing it mysterious like someone is turning her on free because shes such a gone queen) is laying all kinds of stuff on her. When we got to Bixel, it turns out Trudi's daddy has paid for the stuff, including a tin of maryjane and rolls of bees, and hes asked Miss Destiny to take it to her place and Bring Everybody and theyll be up later and we'll have a party. We rode back, and on Broadway the cop-patrol is driving meanly. Skipper put on his dark shades, Chuck lowered his widehat, I sank into the seat (the junk: the roust), and goddamned Miss Destiny waves at the cops—"Yoohoo, girls"—shes flying out of her gay head. Luckily they didnt hear her and they already had someone in back, so they went by with everyone-hating faces. Just as Skipper parked, Trudi's daddy drives up in his tough stationwagon with Trudi behind him wrapped in—I swear—a fur stole—"Like Mae West," she cooed.

And we all went up to Miss Destiny's.

4

Destiny's place is two ugly tight rooms with naileddown windowshades and a head. You climb two narrow stairways and then make your way through a maze of cramped halls

lighted just enough by greasy lightbulbs to reveal the cobwebs and the dirt—long narrow corridors like in the movie-
serial when we were kids: *And the Dragon Lady put Terry
and the Pirates in a narrow hallway and she punched a
button and the walls kept coming closer . . . threatening to
crrrrrrush! everyone to . . . death!!*

Miss Destiny opened the door and turned on the light.
The light screamed in our pupiled eyes, transforming the
cobwebs on the ceiling into long nooselike shadows. Darling
Dolly Dane was curled up on a couch, and Lola and a
seedy-looking soldier were carrying on on another—this is
the kitchen but it has two bedcouches. Lola hollers in her
ugly man's voice turn the fucking lights off. "Put out thy
own dam lights, as the stunning Desdemona said," Miss
Destiny answered. Both the soldier and Lola started adjust-
ing their clothes, and Miss Destiny says arent they Too
Much?—everyone here has seen boys and girls, and besides,
all the world is a swinging stage!

Now Lola goes into the other room, and in a few minutes,
lo and behold! here she is back, in Japanese drag! posing at
the door: kimono with beautiful colored butterflies—sandals
—slanted eyes! and she is saying something like teeny-
vosey which she says means kiss in Chinese—but the soldier
(he playing the stud with her when we walked in) isnt paying her any more attention, and it's obvious, the way hes
looking, that hes a godown fruit serviceman—a not very at-
tractive butch fruit whom Lola thought was a stud (and
queens are fooled more often than they admit). Pissed off,
Lola grabs the soldier's cap, pushes it over his head, and
very much like a rough man shoves him through the door:
"You gotta make reveille, dear!"

And while we're turning on juice and joints and pills—
Trudi's fat daddy saying, "Come on boys, come on turn on"
—palming all of us excitedly—the queens are changing into
high drag in the other room—much more successfully than
Lola. Now Trudi minces out in blacklace negligee, panties
and brassiere (her chest taped to give her real-appearing
cleavage under the falsies)—looking I have to say disturb-
ingly real like one of those girls in the back pages of the
scandal magazines that advertise those slinky gowns and
underclothes with crazy names like tigerlily nightie and
heaven-in-the-boudoir panties and French-frivolity brassiere
—and Darling Dolly Dane is all pink ruffles and queen-

cuteness, and Miss Destiny (being more modest and more the regal type anyway) makes her entrance, last of course, in green satin eveningdress and fluffed out rair with golden sequins. . . .

Right after that, Buddy came in with a score. Miss Destiny says shes sorry but theyll have to use the head. The score is obviously disappointed. A few minutes later and we hear the score coughing spitting. Lola says acidly she despises amateurs and queers. Now they come out, and the score is not only disappointed but nervous, afraid of the scene. As he started toward the door, Trudi calls out, "Dont be nervous, dear—blame the beads!"—and Skipper is going to Talk to him—but Buddy said no he got all the bread himself—and: "Did you hear the square spitting, man? did you?—" indignantly "—Christ, and I only *pretended* to shoot!" Darling Dolly is doing an imitation strip, proud of her smooth girlskin and figure, and everytime she bumps (like the queen at the 1-2-3 earlier), she says, "Sssssssssssssufferrrrrrrrr. . . ." Trudi's daddy is giggling almost hysterically now, opening drinks, passing pills, joints.

Suddenly theres a racket outside the window, like someone throwing a bottle, and Miss Destiny says, "It's that psycho bitch!" and pulls the shades from the nails and theres the sexhungry nympho in the next building hanging out the window in her halfslip and brassiere (and she isnt badlooking) saying whats going on we're disturbing the peace. *Her* piece, giggles Trudi, smothering herself cozily in her stole. And Miss Destiny coos, "Come on over, dear, come on over," to placate her, and the sexhungry woman almost jumps through the window—"I'll be right over, hear?" "Hoddawg!" said Chuck, and this puts Miss Destiny on. In just a few minutes heres the nympho and says it's so warm she'll take off her blouse if you dont mind, and I mean she wasted no time. Appalled at such uncouth effrontery, Darling Dolly Dane, smoking elegantly, inhaled accidentally and almost choked.

To top it all off for Miss Destiny, who was becoming Most Depressed, heres another queen at the door: Miss Bobbi, with a drunk who tries to sober up immediately, rejects the scene, turns to leave—but Skipper gets a chance to Talk to him. "Cool it, cholly," is all Skipper said, and the man reached for his wallet nervously, hands the money to Skipper, and stumbles out hurriedly.

Miss Bobbi says icily hand over the bread which rightly belongs to her. Skipper gave her a nofooling? look. Miss Bobbi says *she* brought the score here, *after all!* Skipper says who got it? Miss Bobbi says she was *going* to until Skipper came on so bigassedly. Skipper says the score would have clipped *her*, and you saw it, jack, the score *gave* the bread to him. Miss Bobbi swished out in a huff.

In absolute depression, Miss Destiny flung herself on the couch crying oh no, "Miss Thing, what are we doing here?" —clinging to a Poor Pitiful Pearl doll on the couch—a sadeyed orphan doll—but everyone was talking and moving and no one paid her any attention. So she freshened up her makeup peering into a tiny stonestudded compact saying shes a mess, and please, to me, sit beside her, *please!* Then she imagined she saw Darling Dolly in the mirror making sexeyes at me, and Miss Destiny says *Well That Is The Limit!* "Darling Dolly Dane is a common whore!" Miss Destiny almost-shouted at me and no one hears her but me, the radio turned on to one of those California night-stations with the smothered rock-n-roll sexmoans, "and all of you! especially you! are just bums! nogood lowlife hobos! who will end up! on Thunderbird! or worse than hobos: hypes! hopelessly hung up and cant get it!" and shes going on very unlike the gay Miss swinging Destiny. "And I! dont! know! what! Iamdoing! here! amongst all this: *tuh-rash*! I! Went!! To College!!! And Read Shakespeare!!!!"

I whispered dont tell anyone, but me too.

"Next youll be the Prince of Wales," she says bitchily, glowering at Chuck and Buddy making up to the nympho, who was fanning herself with her slip now.

And Miss Destiny goes on haughtily—sure of her ground: "Then—tell—me: if you read Shakespeare, Who Is Desdemona?" doubting it superiorly, giving me The Supreme Test: Shakespeare and his queenly he-roines who were first, remember, played by men.

I answered (and remember the pills, the liquor, the maryjane): "Desdemona was a swinging queen in the French Quarter who married a spadestud who dug her until a jealous pusher turned him on that his queen was making it with a studsailor, and the spade smothered the queen Desdemona and the heat came for him and he killed himself. . . ."

Miss Destiny stared at me a long while—not speaking. And

as she was staring at me like that, Lola—who had gone to the head outside, Destiny's being occupied—returned howling theres a man in the head outside and he aint got no pants! Miss Destiny sprang up, rushed at Darling Dolly Dane:

"You dizzy silly cunt! you brought him here didnt you?"

"Where else, Miss Destiny?" Darling Dolly Dane pleads helplessly, covering her face dramatically.

"Go give him his pants!"

"How can I, Destiny? I dont know where I *left* them!"

"*Miss* Destiny!" Miss Destiny screamed.

"*Miss* Destiny dammit!" Darling Dolly Dane shrieked back.

"Here!" Miss Destiny rushes into the other room, comes back with a pair of pants (which turn out later to be Buddy's, who is with the nympho in the other room), empties the pockets on the floor, tosses the pants at Darling Dolly Dane, shouting: "Throw them through the transom!"

Darling Dolly rushes out whimpering.

"Silly bitch," says Miss Destiny, glaring at her when she returns giggling now the man must have thought the pants came from Heaven.

Now Miss Destiny sat on the floor next to me. "You *do* know who Desdemona is!"

Then again there was a long silence between us.

Suddenly!

Suddenly, and strangely—strangely then but not so now: now, inevitably and very clearly like this: Something was released inside Miss Destiny and something established between us in that moment by the simple fact of the mutual knowledge of Desdemona: that something released and that something established which she had yearned for with others from person to person in this locked world—and trying always futilely before, had given up. And of course too it was the liquor, and rejection earlier smashing at her stomach like a huge powerful fist—and the pills pushing-pulling in opposite directions, jarring her—the memory too of the Real girls with whom three of us had gone earlier—and this importantly: the loneliness churning beneath that gay façade desperately every awake moment shouting to be spoken, to be therefore shared: released by something as small as this, the common knowledge of the sad sad tale of Desdemona—or maybe more accurately than released:

say, erupting out of the depths of her consciousness, aroused
by the earlier rejection, resulting in that rare fleeting contact made rarely somehow like a match struck in the dark for
a breathless sputtering instant. . . . And so now, because of
Desdemona and all this meant to Miss Destiny, and all the
things set off from the knowledge, Miss Destiny blurted suddenly frantically:

"Oh God! . . . Sometimes when Im very high and sitting
maybe at the 1-2-3, I imagine that an angel suddenly appears and stands on the balcony where the band is going—or
maybe Im on Main Street or in Pershing Square—and the
angel says, 'All right, boys and girls, this is it, the world is
ending, and Heaven or Hell will be to spend eternity just as
you are now, in the same place among the same people—
Forever!' And hearing this, Im terrified and I know suddenly
what that means—and I start to run but I cant run fast
enough for the evil angel, he sees me and stops me and Im
Caught. . . ."

*(Like in the game of statues long ago and someone swung
you round and round and you stayed frozen as you fell, and
the angel is the swinger now. . . .)*

And Miss Destiny went on desperately:

"And I know it sounds crazy but I came here believing—
no, not really Believing—but hoping maybe, maybe somehow
crazily *hoping!*—that some producer would see me, think I
was Real— Discover me!—make me a Big Star! and I would
go to the dazzling premieres and Louella Hopper would inter-
view me and we would stand in the spotlights and no one
would ever know I wasnt Real—"

*(That impossible strange something that will never hap-
pen. . . .)*

And Miss Destiny rushes on feverishly:

"And at night in bed drowning in the dark, I think tomorrow will be just like today—but I'll be older—or I come
unexpectedly on myself in a mirror or a reflection in a window, and it takes my breath: *Me!!* . . . And I think about my
wedding and how Fabulous I'll be—but I want to fly out of my
skin! jump out! be someone else! so I can leave Miss Destiny
far, far behind. . . ."

*(And Miss Destiny wakes up at night terrified by the knowl-
edge of that strange impossibility, and the darkness screams
Loneliness! and impossibility, whirling around us—and soon*

*youll have to face the morning and yourself—the same,
again. . . .)*

In the other room someone yelled, and it was the nympho.
I heard Chuck shouting Whooooooooppeeeee!! . . . and Darling
Dolly shrieked: "Chuck, get *off!*—thats Buddy!" And Lola
came out rushing yelling at no one, "Leave me alone! Im
ugly! Im ugly!"—her face smeared grotesquely with paint
and enormous tears— "Im ugly, Im ugleeeeeeeee!" and Trudi
trying to soothe her with her fur stole—momentarily leaving
Skipper, who is passed out drunk. . . .

"All this is going on," Miss Destiny sighed, hugging the
orphan doll, "and when tomorrow someone will maybe ask
us, What did you do last night?—we'll answer, Nothing. . . .
And, oh, do you believe in God?" she asks me abruptly, and
I answered it's a cussword. "Oh, yes, my dear," Miss Destiny
said, "there *is* a God, and He is one hell of a joker. Just—
look—" and she indicates her lovely green satin dress and
then waves her hand over the entire room. *"Trapped! . . .*
But one day, in the most lavish drag youve evuh seen—
heels! and gown! and beads! and spangled earrings!— Im
going to storm heaven and protest! *Here I am!!!!!* I'll yell
—and I'll shake my beads at Him. . . . And God will cringe!"

Now Miss Destiny leans toward me and I can smell the
sweet liquor and the sweet . . . lost . . . perfume—and with
a franticness that only abysmal loneliness can produce, she
whispered:

"Marry me please, dear!"

5

I was out in the street with the jazzcat from New York
wearing dark shades who had somehow turned up later at
Destiny's. And Los Angeles was dreary in the earlyhours with
the sidewalks wet where theyve just watered them and the
purplish haze of the early morning. And he asked me which
way I was going. That way, I said. Me too, he said. And
we walked through the streets.

Then somewhere a bell began to sound, and I looked up in-
stinctively at the sky. . . . *One day that bell will sound and
Miss Destiny's evil angel will appear! . . .*

I left Los Angeles without seeing Miss Destiny after that
night. And I went to San Diego, briefly.

And I returned to Los Angeles.

A few of the people I had known were gone—even in that short time—back to the Midwest or to Times Square, or had been busted, or moved to Coffee Andy's in Hollywood, or gone to Golden Miami. They had disappeared, one day: One day youre here and thats fine, and the next day youre gone and thats fine too, and someone has that very day come in to take your place whatever it might have been.

Chuck was still here, boots and widehat. And Skipper . . . And Trudi still blaming it on the beads . . .

I asked Chuck about Miss Destiny, one night, when we were again at the 1-2-3, but this time it was quiet. Not even the juke-box was playing. Everyone was broke. Not a single score. Even the pushers hung dismally inside the bar.

Chuck said he hadnt seen Miss Destiny in a long time, she had just disappeared. Somewhere. "Man, she was a gone queen," he said, pushing his cowboy hat back in a kind of tribute to Miss Destiny.

I asked him did she have her Fabulous Wedding.

"Oh, sure, man, I did not go though—someone tole me about it, she had it out in Hollywood, man, in this real Fine pad, an I heard she akchoolly dressed like a bride, man—she married some studhustler from See-a-dal, and it musta been a real Fine bash, if I re-call Miss Destinee right. . . ."

Then he went on to tell me he had a job washing dishes for a few days but he quit and how some score has promised to put him in some malehouse in Hollywood where he'll make at least $50 a day.

Later I saw Pauline (and now the jukebox was playing the song which I will always think of as part of L.A.: *For Your Love*—and the sad throaty sounds of Ed Townsend meaning it), whom (Pauline) I had met before I left, having found Miss Destiny's warning that first night in the park was justified: Pauline coming on Big with how she would have her own beautyshop in a few weeks and whoever she dug would have it Made and Made Big.

"Let me *tell* you about *Destiny*—" Pauline said. "You *left* before she got *married*—well, she had her wedding all right, she didnt *invite* me, but I *heard,* and it was *Hor-ri-ble.* It was *A-tro-cee-ous.* She had her winding staircase all right, too, and she *stumbled* on her train and *ripped* her veil and came *face down!* Then the place was *raided.* And *thats* where Miss Destiny the college co-ed is now, *busted!*—in the *joint*—*again!*—for *masquerading*—and this is not the first time she gets knocked over so she will be cooling it there *for quite a while!* And can you imagine the *sight?* Miss Destiny in bridal drag sitting crying in the paddy-wagon this is her *wedding day? . . ."*

Trudi claims Miss Destiny is living in Beverly Hills with the man who sponsored the wedding (though Trudi didnt go either, afraid theyd raid it, but they didnt, and she says she wishes now she'd been a beautiful bridesmaid like Destiny asked her, and it broke Destiny's heart when Trudi said no but thats the beads). "And I hear the Destiny looked simply Fabulous in her gown and red hair," says Trudi, "and, honey, it just goes to show you some more about those goddam beads—here the Destiny meets this rich daddy who wants to see a queen get married in drag to a butch studhustler, and the Destiny says does he have a winding staircase? and he does. . . ." Well, anyway, Trudi says, so far as she knows, Miss Destiny is still living in Beverly Hills (Skipper says oh no, Bel Air, if she really made it Big) with the rich daddy and her stud husband.

"The rich cholly," says Skipper knowingly, "I bet he digs Destiny's stud, not Destiny—but he gets kicks watching them make out, jack. You know, hes queer—" and Skipper goes on to tell me how hes tired of the small hustling and how hes ready to push back into the Bigtime—and Trudi says, "Dont be nervous, babe, youll shake the beads."

And so, of Miss Destiny's Wedding there are many versions. No one seems to have gone to it.

But everyone has heard about it.

Only one thing is certain. Miss Destiny is no longer around.

And I wondered if somehow she had escaped her Evil Angel.

And again for a period I avoided the park and the bars—and when I came back, Chuck of course was still around. And now we're sitting in Pershing Square at the same place where I first met Miss Destiny. . . . (And Jenny Lu is in the park too, as if The Angel had got *her* number—woe-*uh!* . . . and Holy Moses . . . and Saint Tex, who outstayed The Word and was reConverted by Saint Thunderbird to California . . . and the five white angel-sisters with Christ still bleeding wax. . . .)

Suddenly Chuck said:

"Oh, man, did you hear about Miss Destinee?—you remember her, that far-out queen with the redhair? Well, man, some queen was saying how she got this letter from Destinee. An remember this ah this ah head doctor she was going to, man?—the one she said she would have on the couch next time? Well, he finally cured Miss Destinee, man —Miss Destinee wrote she ain a queen no more, she has honest-to-jesus-gone-Christ turned *stud*, man!—an that ain all, man!" he goes on gleefully "—Miss Destinee wrote she is getting married, man!—*to a real woman! . . .*"

And Chuck pushed his widehat over his eyes as if to block his sudden vision of a world in which such crazy things can happen.

I imagine Miss Destiny sitting lonesomely in Somewhere, Big City, America—carefully applying her makeup—and I think:

Oh Destiny, Miss Destiny! I dont know whats become of you, nor where you are—but that story Chuck just told me, as you yourself should be the first one to admit, is oh Too Much to believe!

EDWARD ALBEE

The Sandbox

**A BRIEF PLAY, IN MEMORY OF MY
GRANDMOTHER (1876-1959)**

Music by William Flanagan

The Players:

THE YOUNG MAN ...:	25, a good-looking, well-built boy in a bathing suit.
MOMMY	55, a well-dressed, imposing woman.
DADDY	60, a small man; gray, thin.
GRANDMA	86, a tiny, wizened woman with bright eyes.
THE MUSICIAN	No particular age, but young would be nice.

Note:

When, in the course of the play, MOMMY and DADDY call each other by these names, there should be no suggestion of regionalism. These names are of empty affection and point up the pre-senility and vacuity of their characters.

The Scene:

A bare stage, with only the following: Near the footlights, far stage-right, two simple chairs set side by side, facing the audience; near the footlights, far stage-left, a chair facing stage-right with a music stand before it; farther back, and stage-center, slightly elevated and raked, a large child's sandbox with a toy pail and shovel; the background is the sky, which alters from brightest day to deepest night.

At the beginning, it is brightest day; the YOUNG MAN is alone on stage, to the rear of the sandbox, and to one side. He is doing calisthenics; he does calisthenics until quite at the very end of the play. These calisthenics, employing the arms only, should suggest the beating and fluttering of wings. The YOUNG MAN is, after all, the Angel of Death.

MOMMY *and* DADDY *enter from stage-left,* MOMMY *first.*

MOMMY
(*Motioning to* DADDY) Well, here we are; this is the beach.

DADDY (*Whining*)
I'm cold.

MOMMY
(*Dismissing him with a little laugh*) Don't be silly; it's as warm as toast. Look at that nice young man over there: *he* doesn't think it's cold. (*Waves to the* YOUNG MAN) Hello.

YOUNG MAN
(*With an endearing smile*) Hi!

MOMMY (*Looking about*)
This will do perfectly . . . don't you think so, Daddy? There's sand there . . . and the water beyond. What do you think, Daddy?

DADDY (*Vaguely*)
Whatever you say, Mommy.

MOMMY
(*With the same little laugh*) Well, of course . . . whatever
I say. Then, it's settled, is it?

DADDY (*Shrugs*)
She's *your* mother, not mine.

MOMMY
I know she's my mother. What do you take me for? (*A
pause*) All right, now; let's get on with it. (*She shouts into
the wings, stage-left*) You! Out there! You can come in now.
> (*The* MUSICIAN *enters, seats himself in the chair,
> stage-left, places music on the music stand, is ready
> to play.* MOMMY *nods approvingly*)

MOMMY
Very nice; very nice. Are you ready, Daddy? Let's go get
Grandma.

DADDY
Whatever you say, Mommy.

MOMMY
(*Leading the way out, stage-left*) Of course, whatever I
say. (*To the* MUSICIAN) You can begin now.
> (*The* MUSICIAN *begins playing;* MOMMY *and* DADDY
> *exit; the* MUSICIAN, *all the while playing, nods
> to the* YOUNG MAN)

YOUNG MAN
(*With the same endearing smile*) Hi!
> (*After a moment,* MOMMY *and* DADDY *re-enter,
> carrying* GRANDMA. *She is borne in by their hands*

*under her ampits; she is quite rigid; her legs are
drawn up; her feet do not touch the ground; the
expression on her ancient face is that of puzzle-
ment and fear*)

DADDY

Where do we put her?

MOMMY

(*The same little laugh*) Wherever I say, of course. Let me
see . . . well . . . all right, over there . . . in the sandbox.
(*Pause*) Well, what are you waiting for, Daddy? . . . The sandbox!

(*Together they carry* GRANDMA *over to the sandbox and more or less dump her in*)

GRANDMA

(*Righting herself to a sitting position; her voice a cross between a baby's laugh and cry*) Ahhhhhh! Graaaaa!

DADDY (*Dusting himself*)

What do we do now?

MOMMY

(*To the* MUSICIAN) You can stop now.
(*The* MUSICIAN *stops*)
(*Back to* DADDY) What do you mean, what do we do now?
We go over there and sit down, of course. (*To the* YOUNG
MAN) Hello there.

YOUNG MAN

(*Again smiling*) Hi!
(MOMMY *and* DADDY *move to the chairs, stage-right,
and sit down. A pause*)

GRANDMA

(*Same as before*) Ahhhhhh! Ah-haaaaaa! Graaaaaa!

DADDY

Do you think . . . do you think she's . . . comfortable?

MOMMY (*Impatiently*)

How would I know?

DADDY

(*Pause*) What do we do now?

MOMMY

(*As if remembering*) We . . . wait. We . . . sit here . . . and we wait . . . that's what we do.

DADDY

(*After a pause*) Shall we talk to each other?

MOMMY

(*With that little laugh; picking something off her dress*) Well, *you* can talk, if you want to . . . if you can think of anything to *say* . . . if you can think of anything *new*.

DADDY (*Thinks*)

No . . . I suppose not.

MOMMY

(*With a triumphant laugh*) Of course not!

GRANDMA

(*Banging the toy shovel against the pail*) Haaaaaa! Ah-haaaaaa!

MOMMY

(*Out over the audience*) Be quiet, Grandma . . . just be quiet, and wait.

(GRANDMA *throws a shovelful of sand at* MOMMY)

MOMMY

(*Still out over the audience*) She's throwing sand at me! You
stop that, Grandma; you stop throwing sand at Mommy!
(*To* DADDY) She's throwing sand at me.

> (DADDY *looks around at* GRANDMA, *who screams at
> him*)

GRANDMA

GRAAAAA!

MOMMY

Don't look at her. Just . . . sit here . . . be very still . . .
and wait. (*To the* MUSICIAN) You . . . uh . . . you go ahead
and do whatever it is you do.

> (*The* MUSICIAN *plays*)
>
> (MOMMY *and* DADDY *are fixed, staring out beyond the
> audience.* GRANDMA *looks at them, looks at the*
> MUSICIAN, *looks at the sandbox, throws down the
> shovel*)

GRANDMA

Ah-haaaaaa! Graaaaaa! (*Looks for reaction; gets none. Now
. . . directly to the audience*) Honestly! What a way to treat
an old woman! Drag her out of the house . . . stick her in a
car . . . bring her out here from the city . . . dump her in
a pile of sand . . . and leave her here to set. I'm eighty-
six years old! I was married when I was seventeen. To a
farmer. He died when I was thirty. (*To the* MUSICIAN) Will
you stop that, please?

> (*The* MUSICIAN *stops playing*)

I'm a feeble old woman . . . how do you expect anybody
to hear me over that peep! peep! peep! (*To herself*) There's
no respect around here. (*To the* YOUNG MAN) There's no
respect around here!

YOUNG MAN

(*Same smile*) Hi!

GRANDMA

(*After a pause, a mild double-take, continues, to the audience*) My husband died when I was thirty (*indicates* MOMMY), and I had to raise that big cow over there all by my lonesome. You can imagine what *that was like*. Lordy! (*To the* YOUNG MAN) Where'd they get *you?*

YOUNG MAN

Oh . . . I've been around for a while.

GRANDMA

I'll bet you have! Heh, heh, heh. Will you look at you!

YOUNG MAN

(*Flexing his muscles*) Isn't that something? (*Continues his calisthenics*)

GRANDMA

Boy, oh boy; I'll say. Pretty good.

YOUNG MAN (*Sweetly*)

I'll say.

GRANDMA

Where ya from?

YOUNG MAN

Southern California.

GRANDMA (*Nodding*)

Figgers; figgers. What's your name, honey?

YOUNG MAN

I don't know. . . .

GRANDMA

(*To the audience*) Bright, too!

YOUNG MAN

I mean . . . I mean, they haven't given me one yet . . .
the studio . . .

GRANDMA

(*Giving him the once-over*) You don't say . . . you don't
say. Well . . . uh, I've got to talk some more . . . don't
you go 'way.

YOUNG MAN

Oh, no.

GRANDMA

(*Turning her attention back to the audience*) Fine; fine.
(*Then, once more, back to the* YOUNG MAN) You're . . .
you're an actor, hunh?

YOUNG MAN (*Beaming*)

Yes. I am.

GRANDMA

(*To the audience again; shrugs*) I'm smart that way. *Anyhow,* I had to raise . . . *that* over there all by my lonesome;
and what's next to her there . . . that's what she married.
Rich? I tell you . . . money, money, money. They took me off
the *farm* . . . which was real decent of them . . . and they
moved me into the big town house with *them* . . . fixed a
nice place for me under the stove . . . gave me an
army blanket . . . and my own dish . . . my very own dish!
So, what have I got to complain about? Nothing, of course.
I'm not complaining. (*She looks up at the sky, shouts to
someone off stage*) Shouldn't it be getting dark now, dear?
   (*The lights dim; night comes on. The* MUSICIAN *begins to play; it becomes deepest night. There are*

spots on all the players, including the YOUNG MAN, *who is, of course, continuing his calisthenics*)

DADDY (*Stirring*)

It's nighttime.

MOMMY

Shhhh. Be still . . . wait.

DADDY (*Whining*)

It's so hot.

MOMMY

Shhhhhh. Be still . . . wait.

GRANDMA

(*To herself*) That's better. Night. (*To the* MUSICIAN) Honey, do you play all through this part?
(*The* MUSICIAN *nods*)
Well, keep it nice and soft; that's a good boy.
(*The* MUSICIAN *nods again; plays softly*)
That's nice.
(*There is an off-stage rumble*)

DADDY (*Starting*)

What was that?

MOMMY

(*Beginning to weep*) It was nothing.

DADDY

It was . . . it was . . . thunder . . . or a wave breaking . . . or something.

MOMMY

(*Whispering, through her tears*) It was an off-stage rumble . . . and you know what *that* means. . . .

DADDY

I forget. . . .

MOMMY

(*Barely able to talk*) It means the time has come for poor Grandma . . . and I can't bear it!

DADDY (*Vacantly*)

I . . . I suppose you've got to be brave.

GRANDMA (*Mocking*)

That's right, kid; be brave. You'll bear up; you'll get over it.
(*Another off-stage rumble . . . louder*)

MOMMY

Ohhhhhhhhhh . . . poor Grandma . . . poor Grandma. . . .

GRANDMA (*To* MOMMY)

I'm fine! I'm all right! It hasn't happened yet!
(*A violent off-stage rumble. All the lights go out, save the spot on the* YOUNG MAN; *the* MUSICIAN *stops playing*)

MOMMY

Ohhhhhhhhhh. . . . Ohhhhhhhhhh. . . .
(*Silence*)

GRANDMA

Don't put the lights up yet . . . I'm not ready; I'm not quite ready. (*Silence*) All right, dear . . . I'm about done.
(*The lights come up again, to brightest day; the* MUSICIAN *begins to play.* GRANDMA *is discovered, still*

in the sandbox, lying on her side, propped up on an elbow, half covered, busily shoveling sand over herself)

GRANDMA *(Muttering)*

I don't know how I'm supposed to do anything with this goddam toy shovel. . . .

DADDY

Mommy! It's daylight!

MOMMY *(Brightly)*

So it is! Well! Our long night is over. We must put away our tears, take off our mourning . . . and face the future. It's our duty.

GRANDMA

(Still shoveling; mimicking) . . . take off our mourning . . . face the future. . . . Lordy!

(MOMMY and DADDY rise, stretch. MOMMY waves to the YOUNG MAN)

YOUNG MAN

(With that smile) Hi!

(GRANDMA plays dead. (!) MOMMY and DADDY go over to look at her; she is a little more than half buried in the sand; the toy shovel is in her hands, which are crossed on her breast)

MOMMY

(Before the sandbox; shaking her head) Lovely! It's . . . it's hard to be sad . . . she looks . . . so happy. *(With pride and conviction)* It pays to do things well. *(To the MUSICIAN)* All right, you can stop now, if you want to. I mean, stay around for a swim, or something; it's all right with us. *(She sighs heavily)* Well, Daddy . . . off we go.

DADDY

Brave Mommy!

MOMMY

Brave Daddy!

(They exit, stage-left)

GRANDMA

(*After they leave; lying quite still*) It pays to do things well.
... Boy, oh boy! (*She tries to sit up*) ... well, kids ... (*but
she finds she can't*) ... I ... I can't get up. I ... I can't
move. ...

> (*The* YOUNG MAN *stops his calisthenics, nods to the*
> MUSICIAN, *walks over to* GRANDMA, *kneels down by*
> *the sandbox*)

GRANDMA

I ... can't move. ...

YOUNG MAN

Shhhhh ... be very still. ...

GRANDMA

I ... I can't move. ...

YOUNG MAN

Uh ... ma'am; I ... I have a line here.

GRANDMA

Oh, I'm sorry, sweetie; you go right ahead.

YOUNG MAN

I am ... uh ...

GRANDMA

Take your time, dear.

YOUNG MAN

(*Prepares; delivers the line like a real amateur*) I am the
Angel of Death. I am ... uh ... I am come for you.

GRANDMA

What ... wha ... (*Then, with resignation*) ... ohhhh ...
ohhhh, I see.

> (*The* YOUNG MAN *bends over, kisses* GRANDMA *gently*
> *on the forehead*)

GRANDMA

(*Her eyes closed, her hands folded on her breast again, the shovel between her hands, a sweet smile on her face*)

Well. . . . that was very nice, dear. . . .

YOUNG MAN

(*Still kneeling*) Shhhhhh . . . be still. . . .

GRANDMA

What I meant was . . . you did that very well, dear. . . .

YOUNG MAN (*Blushing*)

. . . oh . . .

GRANDMA

No; I mean it. You've got that . . . you've got a quality.

YOUNG MAN

(*With his endearing smile*) Oh . . . thank you; thank you very much . . . ma'am.

GRANDMA

(*Slowly; softly—as the* YOUNG MAN *puts his hands on top of* GRANDMA'S) You're . . . you're welcome . . . dear.

(*Tableau. The* MUSICIAN *continues to play as the curtain slowly comes down*)

CURTAIN

JOHN BARTH

≋≋≋≋≋≋≋≋≋≋≋≋

from The Sot-Weed Factor

THE MOMENTOUS WAGER BETWEEN
EBENEZER AND BEN OLIVER, AND ITS
UNCOMMON RESULT

Pimp in Ebenezer's circle was one wiry, red-haired, be-
freckled ex-Dubliner named John McEvoy, twenty-one years
old and devoid of school education, as long in energy and
resourcefulness as short in money and stature, who spent
his days abed, his evenings pimping for his privileged companions, and the greater part of his nights composing airs
for the lute and flute, and who from the world of things
that men have valued prized none but three: his mistress
Joan Toast (who, whore as well, was both his love and his
living), his music, and his liberty. No one-crown frisker Joan,
but a two-guinea hen well worth the gold to bed her, as
knew every man among them but Ebenezer; she loved her
John for all he was her pimp, and he her truly too for all
she was his whore—for no man was ever *just* a pimp, nor
any woman *merely* whore. They seemed, in fact, a devoted
couple, and jealous.

All spirit, imagination, and brave brown eyes, small-
framed, large-breasted, and tight-skinned (though truly somewhat coarse-pored, and stringy in the hair, and with teeth
none of the best), this Joan Toast was his for the night
who'd two guineas to take her for, and indignify her as he
would, she'd give him his gold's worth and more, for she

took that pleasure in her work as were she the buyer and he the vendor; but come morning she was cold as a fish and back to her Johnny McEvoy, and should her lover of the night past so much as wink eye at her in the light of day, there was no more Joan Toast for *him* at any price.

Ebenezer had of course observed her for some years as she and his companions came and went in their harlotry, and from the talk in the coffee-house had got to know about her in great detail at second hand a number of things that his personal disorganization precluded learning at first. When in manly moments he thought of her at all it was merely as a tart whom, should he one day find himself single-minded enough, it might be sweet to hire to initiate him at long last into the mysteries. For it happened that, though near thirty, Ebenezer was yet a virgin, and this for the reason explained in the previous chapters, that he was no person at all: he could picture any kind of man taking a woman—the bold as well as the bashful, the clean green boy and the dottering gray lecher—and work out in his mind the speeches appropriate to each under any of several sorts of circumstances. But because he felt himself no more one of these than another and admired all, when a situation presented itself he could never choose one role to play over all the rest he knew, and so always ended up either turning down the chance or, what was more usually the case, retreating gracelessly and in confusion, if not always embarrassment. Generally, therefore, women did not give him a second glance, not because he was uncomely—he had marked well that some of the greatest seducers have the faces of goats and the manner of lizards—but because, a woman having taken in his ungainly physique, there remained no other thing for her to notice.

Indeed he might have gone virgin to his grave—for there are urgencies that will be heeded if not one way then perforce another, and that same knuckly hand that penned him his couplets took no wooing to make his quick mistress—but on this March night in 1694 he was noticed by Joan Toast, in the following manner: the gallants were sitting in a ring at Locket's, as was their custom, drinking wine, gossiping, and boasting their conquests, both of the muse and of lesser wenches. There were Dick Merriweather, Tom Trent, and Ben Oliver already well wined, Johnny McEvoy and Joan Toast out for a customer, and Ebenezer incommunicado.

"Heigh-ho!" sighed Dick at a lull in their talk. " 'Twere a

world one could live in did wealth follow wit, for gold's the best bait to snare sweet conies with, and then we poets were fearsome trappers all!"

"No need gold," replied Ben, "did God but give women half an eye for their interests. What makes your good lover, if not fire and fancy? And for whom if not us poets are fire and fancy the very stock in trade? From which 'tis clear, that of all men the poet is most to be desired as a lover: if his mistress have beauty, his is the eye will most be gladdened by't; if she have it not, his is the imagination that best can mask its lack. If she displease him, and he slough her off shortly, she hath at least had for a time the best that woman can get; if she please him, he will haply fix her beauty for good and all in verse, where neither age nor pox can spoil it. And as poets as a class are to be desired in this respect over other sorts of fellows, so should the best poet prove the best lover; were women wise to their interests they'd make seeking him out their life-work, and finding him would straight lay their favors a-quiver in his lap—nay, upon his very writing-desk—and beg him to look on 'em kindly!"

"Out on't, then!" said Dick to Joan Toast. "Ben speaks truly, and 'tis you shall pay *me* two guineas this night! Marry, and were't not that I am poor as any church mouse this week and have not long to live, you'd not buy immortality so cheap! My counsel is to snatch the bargain while it lasts, for a poet cannot long abide this world."

To which Joan rejoined without heat, "Fogh! Could any man of ye rhyme as light as talk, or swive grand as swagger, why, your verse'd be on every lip in London and your arse in every bed, I swear! But *Talk pays no toll*: I look to pacify nor ear nor bum with aught o' ye but my sweet John, who struts not a strut nor brags no brags, but saves words for his melodies and strength for the bed."

"Hi!" applauded Ben. "Well put!"

"If ill timed," John McEvoy added, frowning lightly upon her. "Let no such sentiments come 'twixt thee and two guineas this night, love, or thy sweet John'll have nor strength nor song, but a mere rumbly gut to bed ye with on the morrow."

" 'Sblood!" remarked Tom Trent without emotion. "If Lady Joan reason rightly, there's one among us who far more merits her favor than you, McEvoy, for as you speak one word to our two, so speak you ten to his one: I mean yon Ebenezer, who for lack of words should be chiefest poet and cocksman in this or any winehouse—John Milton and Don Juan Tenorio in a single skin!"

"Indeed he may be," vowed Joan, who, being by chance seated next to Ebenezer, gave him a pat on the hand.

"At any rate," smiled McEvoy, "having heard not a line of his making, I've no evidence he's not a poet."

"Nor I he's not that other," Joan added smartly, "and 'tis more praise on both counts than I can praise the rest o' ye." Then she colored somewhat and added: "I must own I've heard it said, *Marry fat but love lean,* for as how your fat fellow is most often a jolly and patient husband, but your bony lank is long all over and springy in the bed. Howbeit, I've no proof of the thing."

"Then 'sdeath, you shall have it!" cried Ben Oliver, "for there's more to extension than simple length. When the subject in hand's the tool of love, prithee give weight to the matter of diameter, for diameter's what gives weight to love's tool—whether 'tis in hand or in the subject, for that matter! Nay, lass, I'll stick by my fat, as't hath stuck by me. *A plump cock's the very devil of the hen house,* so they say: he treads 'em with authority!"

"'Tis too weighty a question to leave unsettled," declared McEvoy. "What think you, Tom?"

"I take no interest in affairs of the flesh," said Tom, "but I have e'er observed that women, like men, have chiefest relish in things forbidden, and prize no conquest like that of a priest or saint. 'Tis my guess, moreover, that they find their trophy doubly sweet, inasmuch as 'tis hard come by to begin with, and when got 'tis fresh and potent as vintage brandy, for having been so long bottled and corked."

"Dick?"

"I see no sense in it," Merriweather said. "'Tis not a man's weight, but his circumstances, that make him a lover. The sweetest lover of all, I should think, is the man about to end his life, who would by the act of love bid his adieu to this world, and at the moment of greatest heat pass on the next."

"Well, now," McEvoy said, "ye owe it to England to put an answer to't. What I propose is this, that ye put each your best foot forward, so to speak, this same night, and let Joan take eight guinea from him she names loser. Thus the winner gets glory for him and his kind and a swiving to boot; the losers get still a swiving—ay, a double swiving!—and my good woman and I get chops instead of chitterlings for a day. Done?"

"Not I," said Tom. " 'Tis a sorry sport, is lust, that makes man a slavering animal on embracing his mistress and a dolorous vegetable after."

"Nor I," said Dick, "for had I eight guineas I'd hire three trollops and a bottle of Madeira for one final debauch ere I end my life."

"Marry, 'tis done for all o' me," said Ben, "and heartily, too, for your Joan's had none of old Ben these two months past."

"Nor shall I more," swore Joan cheerfully, "for thou'rt a sweatbox and a stinkard, sir. My memory of our last will serve as *your* performance, when I came away bruised and abused as a spaniel bitch from a boar's pen, and had need of a course of liniments to drive out the aches and a course of hot baths to carry off the smell. For the rest of the wager, 'tis Mr. Cooke's to yea or nay."

"So be't," shrugged Ben, "though had I known at the time 'twas that studding I'd be judged by, you'd have found me more bull than boar and haply have a Minotaur to show for't. What say you, Ebenezer?"

Now Ebenezer had followed this raillery intently and would have joined in it, perhaps, but that from his overstocked wardrobe no particular style came readily to hand. Then, when Joan Toast touched him, the hand she touched tingled as if galvanized, and on the instant Ebenezer felt his soul rise up in answer. Had not Boyle shown, and Burlingame taught, that electrical attraction takes place in a vacuum? Well, here was Boyle figured in the empty poet: the pert girl worked some queer attraction in him, called forth a spark from the vacuum of his character, and set him all suddenly a-burn and a-buzz.

But did this prick-up afford the man identity? On the contrary: as he saw the direction the twitting took and heard McEvoy give birth to the wager, he but buzzed and burned the more; his mind ran madly to no end like a rat in a race and could not engage the situation. His sensibility all erected and hard at attention, he could feel the moment coming when the eyes of all would swing to bear on him with some question which he'd be expected to answer. It was the wait for it, together with the tingle of Joan Toast's touch and the rush to find a face to meet the wager with, that made him sick when his ears heard Ben's "What say you,

Ebenezer?" and his two eyes saw ten look to him for reply.

What say? What say? His windpipe glotted with a surfeit of alternatives; but did he urge one up like a low-pressured belch, the suck of the rest ungassed it. Eyes grew quizzical; smiles changed character. Ebenezer reddened, not from embarrassment but from internal pressure.

"What ails ye, friend?" McEvoy.

"Speak up, man!" Ben Oliver.

" 'Swounds! He'll pop!" Dick Merriweather.

One Cooke eyebrow fluttered. A mouth-corner ticked. He closed and unclosed his hands and his mouth, and the strain near retched him, but it was all a dry heave, a false labor: no person issued from it. He gaped and sweated.

"Gah," he said.

" 'Sblood!" Tom Trent. "He's ill! 'Tis the vapors! The fellow wants a clyster!"

"Gah," said Ebenezer again, and then froze tight and said no more, nor moved a single muscle.

By this time his behavior had been noticed by the other patrons of the winehouse, and a number of the curious gathered round him where he sat, now rigid as a statue.

"Hi, there, throw't off!" demanded one fellow, snapping his fingers directly before Ebenezer's face.

" 'Tis the wine has dagged him, belike," a wag suggested, and tweaked the poet's nose, also without effect. "Aye," he affirmed, "the lad's bepickled himself with't. Mark ye, 'tis the fate awaits us all!"

"As you please," declared Ben Oliver with a grin; "I say 'tis a plain case of the staggering fearfuls, and I claim the victory by default, and there's an end on't."

"Aye, but what doth it profit you?" Dick Merriweather asked.

"What else but Joan Toast this night?" laughed Ben, slapping three guineas onto the table. "Upon your honor as judge, John McEvoy, will you refuse me? Test my coins, fellow: they'll ring true as the next man's, and there's three of 'em."

McEvoy shrugged his shoulders and looked inquiringly at his Joan.

"Not in a pig's arse," she sniffed. She flounced from her chair and with a wink at the company flung her arms around Ebenezer's neck and caressed his cheek.

"Ah, me ducky, me dove!" she cooed. "Will ye leave me

to the mercies of yon tub o' suet, to lard like any poor partridge? Save me, sir!"

But Ebenezer sat unmoved and unmoving.

" 'Tis no lardoon thou'rt in for," Ben said. " 'Tis the very spit!"

"Ah! Ah!" cried Joan as though terrified and, clambering onto Ebenezer's lap, hid her face in his neck. "I shake and I shiver!"

The company shouted with delight. Joan grasped one of Ebenezer's large ears in each hand and drew his face nose to nose with her own.

"Carry me off!" she implored him.

"To the spit with her!" urged an onlooker. "Baste the hussy!"

"Aye," said Ben, and crooked his finger at her. "Come along now, sweetmeat."

"As ye be a man and a poet, Eben Cooke," Joan scolded, jumping to her feet and shouting in his ear, "I lay it upon ye to match this rascal's gold with your own and have done with't. If ye will not speak up and act the man, I'm Ben's and be damned t'ye!"

Ebenezer gave a slight start and suddenly stood up, blinking as if just roused from bed. His features twitched, and he alternately blushed and paled as he opened his mouth to speak.

"I had five guineas but this morning by messenger from my father," he said weakly.

"Thou'rt a fool," said Dick Merriweather. "She asks but three, and had you spoke sooner 'twould've cost you but two!"

"Will ye raise him two bob, Ben?" asked John McEvoy, who had been watching the proceedings serenely.

"Indeed he shan't!" snapped Joan. "Is this a horse auction, then, and I a mare to be rid by the high bidder?" She took Ebenezer's arm fondly. "Only match Ben's three guineas, ducky, and speak no more of't. The night's near done, and I am ill o' this lewd raillery."

Ebenezer gawked, swallowed, and shifted his weight.

"I cannot match it here," he said, "for I've but a crown in my purse." He glanced around him wildly. "The money is in my rooms," he added, teetering as if to swoon. "Come with me there, and you shall have't all."

"Hello, the lad's no fool!" said Tom Trent. "He knows a thing or two!"

" 'Sblood, a very Jew!" agreed Dick Merriweather.

"Better a fowl in hand than two flying," Ben Oliver laughed, and jingled his three guineas. " 'Tis a hoax and fraud, to lure honest women to their ruin! What would your father say, Ebenezer, did he get wind of't? Shame, shame!"

"Pay the great ass no heed," said Joan.

Ebenezer swayed again, and several of the company tittered.

"I swear to you——" he began.

"Shame! Shame!" cried Ben once more, wagging a fat finger at him to the company's delight.

Ebenezer tried again, but could do no more than raise his hand and let it fall.

"Stand off!" someone warned uneasily. "He is starching up again!"

"Shame!" roared Ben.

Ebenezer goggled at Joan Toast for a second and then lurched full speed across the room and out of the winehouse.

THE CONVERSATION BETWEEN EBENEZER AND THE WHORE JOAN TOAST, INCLUDING THE TALE OF THE GREAT TOM LEECH.

As a rule Ebenezer would after such a bumble have been in for some hours of motionless reflection in his room. It was his habit (for such rigidities as this at Locket's were not new to him) upon recovering himself to sit at his writing-desk, looking-glass in hand, and stare fish-eyed at his face, which only during such spells was still. But this time, though he did indeed take up his vis-à-vis, the face he regarded was anything but vacant: on the contrary, where typically he'd have seen a countenance blank as an owl's, now he saw a roil as of swallows round a chimney pot; whereas another time he'd have heard in his head but a cosmic rustle, as though his skull were a stranded wentletrap, now he sweated, blushed, and dreamed two score ragged dreams. He studied the ears Joan Toast had touched, as though by study to restore their tingle, and when he could by no means succeed, he recognized with alarm that it was his heart she now had hands on.

"Ah God," he cried aloud, "that I'd risen to the wager!"

The manly sound of his voice arrested him. Moreover, it was the first time he'd ever spoken to himself aloud, and he failed to be embarrassed by it.

"Had I but another chance," he declared to himself, " 'twould be no chore to snatch the moment! Lord, into what ferment have those eyes put me! Into what heat those bosoms!"

He took up the glass again, made himself a face, and inquired, "Who art thou *now*, queer fellow? Hi, there is a twitch in thy blood, I see—a fidget in thy soul! 'Twere a right manly man Joan Toast would taste, were the wench but here to taste him!"

It occurred to him to return to Locket's to seek her out, on the chance she'd not have succumbed to Ben Oliver's entreaties. But he was reluctant to confront his friends so soon after his flight, in the first place, and in the second——

"Curse me for my innocence!" he railed, pounding his fist upon some blank papers on the writing-desk. "What knowledge have I of such things? Suppose she should come with me? 'Sblood! What then?

"Yet 'tis now or never," he told himself grimly. "This Joan Toast sees in me what no woman hath before, nor I myself: a man like other men. And for aught I know she hath made me one, for when else have I talked to myself? When else felt so potent? To Locket's," he ordered himself, "or go virgin to the grave!"

Nevertheless he did not get up, but lapsed instead into lecherous, complicated reveries of rescue and gratitude; of shipwreck or plague and mutual survivorship; of abduction, flight, and violent assault; and, sweetest of all, of towering fame and casual indulgence. When at length he realized that he was not going to Locket's at all, he was overcome with self-loathing and returned, in despair, once more to the mirror.

He calmed at the sight of the face in it.

"Odd fellow, there! *Ooo-ooo!* Hey-nonny-nonny! *Fa-la!*"

He leered and mouthed into the glass until his eyes brimmed with tears, and then, exhausted, buried his face in his long arms. Presently he fell asleep.

There came, an uncertain time later, a knocking at the entrance door below, and before Ebenezer was awake enough to wonder at it, his own door was opened by his servant,

Bertrand, who had been sent to him just a few days earlier by his father. This Bertrand was a thin-faced, wide-eyed bachelor in his later forties whom Ebenezer knew scarcely at all, for Andrew had hired him while the young man was still at Cambridge. With him, when he had come from the St. Giles establishment, he had brought the following note from Andrew, in an envelope sealed with wax:

Ebenezer,
 The Bearer of this note is Bertrand Burton, my Valet since 1686, and now yours, if you want him. He is a diligent enough fellow, if something presumptuous, and will make you a good man if you hold him to his place. Mrs Twigg and he got on ill together, to the point where I had either to sack him or lose her, without whom I could scarce manage my house. Yet deeming it a hard matter to sack the fellow outright, whose only fault is, that though he never forgets his work, he oft forgets his place, I have promoted him out of my service into yours. I shall pay him his first quarters wage; after that, if you want him, I presume your post with Paggen will afford him.

Though his current wage from Peter Paggen, which was precisely what it had been in 1688, was barely adequate to keep himself, Ebenezer nonetheless had welcomed Bertrand's service, at least for the three months during which it was to cost him nothing. Luckily, the room adjoining his own was unoccupied at the time, and he had arranged with his landlord for Bertrand to lodge there, where he was always within call.

Now the man stepped into the room in nightshirt and cap, all smiles and winks, said, "A lady to see you, sir," and, to Ebenezer's great surprise, ushered Joan Toast herself into the room.

"I shall retire at once," he announced, winking again, and left them before Ebenezer could recover sufficiently to protest. He was extremely embarrassed and not a little alarmed at being alone with her, but Joan, not a whit disturbed, came over to where he still sat at the writing table and bussed him lightly upon the cheek.

"Say not a word," she ordered, taking off her hat. "I know well I'm tardy, and I ask your pardon for't."

Ebenezer sat dumb, too astonished to speak. Joan strode

blithely to the windows, closed the curtains, and commenced undressing.

" 'Tis your friend Ben Oliver's to blame, with his *three* guineas, and his *four* guineas, and his *five* guineas, and his great hands both a-clench to lay hold on me! But a shilling o'er your five he couldn't offer, or wouldn't, and since 'twas you first offered it, I'm quit o' the brute with conscience clear."

Ebenezer stared at her, head afire.

"Come along now, sweet," Joan said presently, and turned to him entirely unclothed. "Put thy guineas upon the table and let's to bed. Faith, but there's a nip in the air this night! *Brrr!* Jump to't, now!" She sprang to the bed and snuggled under the coverlets, drawing them up around her chin.

"Come along!" she said again, a bit more briskly.

"Ah God, I cannot!" Ebenezer said. His face was rapturous, his eyes were wild.

"Ye *what?*" Joan cried, throwing back the covers and sitting up in alarm.

"I cannot pay thee," Ebenezer declared.

"Not pay me! What prank is this, sir, ye make me butt of, when I have put off Ben Oliver and his five gold guineas? Out with thy money now, Master Cooke, and off with thy breeches, and prank me no pranks!"

" 'Tis no prank, Joan Toast," said Ebenezer. "I cannot pay thee five guineas, or four guineas, or three. I cannot pay thee a shilling. Nay, not so much as a farthing."

"What! Are ye paupered, then?" She gripped his shoulders as if to shake him. "Marry, sir, open wide those great cow's eyes, that I may claw them from out their sockets! Think ye to make a fool o' me?" She swung her legs over the side of the bed.

"Nay, nay, lady!" Ebenezer cried, falling to his knees before her. "Nay, I have the five guineas, and more. But how price the priceless? How buy Heaven with simple gold? Ah, Joan Toast, ask me not to cheapen thee so! Was't for gold that silver-footed Thetis shared the bed of Peleus, Achilles' sire? Think thee Venus and Anchises did their amorous work on consideration of five guineas? Nay, sweet Joan, a man seeks not in the market for the favors of a goddess!"

"Let foreign bawds run their business as't please 'em," Joan declared, somewhat calmer. " 'Tis five guineas the night for this one, and pay ere ye play. Do ye reckon it cheap, then pleasure in thy bargain: 'tis all one to me. What a temper ye put me in with thy *not a farthing!* I had near leaped ye! Come along, now, and save thy conceits for a love sonnet in the morning."

"Ah, dear God, Joan, wilt thou not see?" said Ebenezer, still down upon his knees. " 'Tis not for common sport I crave thee, as might another: such lechery I leave to mere gluttonous whoremongers like Ben Oliver. What I crave of thee cannot be bought!"

"Aha," smiled Joan, "so 'tis a matter o' strange tastes, is't? I'd not have guessed it by the honest look o' ye, but think not so quickly 'tis out o' the question. Well do I know *There's more ways to the woods than one,* and if't work no great or lasting hurt, why, 'tis but a matter o' price to me, sir. Name me thy game, and I'll fix thee thy fee."

"Joan, Joan, put by this talk!" cried Ebenezer, shaking his head. "Can you not see it tears my heart? What's past is past; I cannot bear to think on't, how much the less hear it from thy sweet lips! Dear girl, I swear to thee now I am a virgin, and as I come to thee pure and undefiled, so in my mind you come to me; whate'er hath gone before, speak not of it. Nay!" he warned, for Joan's mouth dropped open. "Nay, not a word of't, for 'tis over and done. Joan Toast, I *love* thee! Ah, that startles thee! Aye, I swear to Heaven I love thee, and 'twas to declare it I wished thee here. Speak no more of your awful trafficking, for I love thy sweet body unspeakably, and that spirit which it so fairly houses, unimaginably!"

"Nay, Mr. Cooke, 'tis an unbecoming jest ye make, to call thyself virgin," Joan said doubtfully.

"As God is my witness," swore Ebenezer, "I have known no woman carnally to this night, nor ever loved at all."

"But how is that?" Joan demanded. "Why, when I was but a slip of a thing, not yet fourteen and innocent of the world's villainy, I recall I once cried out at table how I had commenced a queer letting of blood, and what was I ill of? And send quick for the leeches! And everyone laughed and made strange jests, but none would tell me what was the cause of't. Then my young bachelor uncle Harold approached me privily, and kissed me upon the lips and stroked my hair, and told me 'twas no common leech I wanted, for that I was letting much blood already; but that anon when I had stopped I should come to him in secret, for he kept in his rooms a great tom leech such as I had ne'er yet been bit by, the virtue of which was, that it would restore by sweet infusions what I had lost. I believed without question all that he told me, for he was a great favorite o' mine, more brother than uncle to me, and therefore I said naught to anyone, but directly the curse left me went straight to his bedchamber, as he had prescribed. 'Where is the great tom leech?' I asked him. 'I have't ready,' said he, 'but it fears the light and will do its work only in darkness. Make thyself ready,' said he, 'and I'll apply the leech where it must go.' 'Very well,' said I, 'but ye must tell me how to ready myself, Harold, for I know naught of leeching.' 'Disrobe thyself,' said he, 'and lie down upon the bed.'

"And so I stripped myself all naked, simple soul that I was, right before his eyes, and lay down upon the bed as he directed—a skinny pup I, as yet unbreasted and unfurred—and he blew out the candle. 'Ah, dear Harold!' I cried. 'Come lie beside me on the bed, I pray, for I fear the bite o' thy great tom leech in the dark!' Harold made me no answer, but shortly joined me upon his bed. 'How is this?' I cried, feeling his skin upon me. 'Do you mean to take the leech as well? Did you too lose blood?' 'Nay,' he laughed, ' 'tis but the manner whereby my leech must be applied. I have't ready for ye, dear girl; are ye ready for't?' 'Nay, dear Harold,' I cried, 'I am fearful! Where will it bite me? How will it hurt?' ' 'Twill bite where it must,' said Harold, 'and 'twill pain ye a mere minute, and then pleasure ye enough.' 'Ah, then,' I sighed, 'let us get by the pain and hasten the pleasure with all speed. But prithee hold my hand, lest I cry out at the creature's bite.' 'Ye shan't cry out,' Harold said then, 'for I shall kiss ye.'

"And straightway he embraced me and kissed my mouth tight shut, and, while we were a-kissing, suddenly I felt the great tom leech his fearful bite, and I was maiden no more! At first I wept, not alone from the pain he'd warned of, but from alarm at what I'd learned o' the leech's nature. But e'en as Harold promised, the pain soon flew, and his great tom leech took bite after bite till near sunup, by which time, though I was by no means weary o' the leeching, my Harold had no more leech to leech with, but only a poor cockroach or simple pismire, not fit for the work, which scurried away at the first light. 'Twas then I learned the queer virtue o' this animal: for just as a fleabite, the more ye scratch it, wants scratching the more, so, once this creature had bit me, I longed for further bites and was forever after poor Harold and his leech, like an opium eater his phial. And though since then I've suffered the bite of every sort and size—none more fearsome or ravenous than my good John's—yet the craving plagues me still, till I shiver at the thought o' the great tom leech!"

"Stop, I beg thee!" Ebenezer pleaded. "I cannot hear more! What, 'Dear Uncle,' you call him, and 'Poor Harold'! Ah, the knave, the scoundrel, to deceive you so, who loved and trusted him! 'Twas no *leechery* he put thee to, but *lechery*, and laid thy maiden body forever in the bed of harlotry! I curse him, and his ilk!"

"Ye say't with relish," smiled Joan, "as one who'd do the like with fire in his eye and sweat on his arse, could he find himself a child fond as I. Nay, Ebenezer, rail not at poor dear Harold, who is these several years under the sod from an ague got swiving ardently in cold chambers. Says I, 'tis but the nature o' the leech to bite and of the leeched to want biting, and 'tis a mystery and astonishment to me, since so many crave leeching and the best leech is so lightly surfeited, how yours hath gone starved, as ye declare, these thirty years! What, are ye a mere arrant sluggard, sir? Or are ye haply o' that queer sort who lust for none but their own sex? 'Tis a thing past grasping!"

"Nor the one nor the other," replied Ebenezer. "I am man in spirit as well as body, and my innocence is not wholly my own choosing. I have ere now been ready enough, but to grind love's grain wants mortar as well as pestle; no man dances the morris dance alone, and till this night no woman e'er looked on me with favor."

"Marry!" laughed Joan. "Doth the ewe chase the ram, or the hen the cock? Doth the field come to the plow for furrowing, or the scabbard to the sword for sheathing? 'Tis all arsy-turvy ye look at the world!"

"That I grant," sighed Ebenezer, "but I know naught of the art of seduction, nor have the patience for't."

"Fogh! There's no great labor to the bedding of women! For the most, all a man need do, I swear, is ask plainly and politely, did he but know it."

"How is that?" exclaimed Ebenezer in astonishment. "Are women then so lecherous?"

"Nay," said Joan. "Think not we crave a swiving pure and

simple at any time as do men always—'tis oft a pleasure with us, but rarely a passion. Howbeit, what with men forever panting at us like so many hounds at a salt-bitch, and begging us put by our virtue and give 'em a tumble, and withal despising us for whores and slatterns if we do; or bidding us be faithful to our husbands and yet losing no chance to cuckold their truest friends; or charging us to guard our chastity and yet assaulting it from all quarters in every alleyway, carriage, or sitting room; or being soon bored with us if we show no fire in swiving and yet sermoning us for sinners if we do; inventing morals on the one hand and rape on the other; and in general preaching us to virtue whilst they lure us on to vice—what with the pull and haul of all this, I say, we women are forever at sixes and sevens, all fussed and rattled and torn 'twixt what we ought and what we would, and so entirely confounded, that we never know what we think on the matter or how much license to grant from one minute to the next; so that if a man commence the usual strut, pat, and tweak, we may thrust him from us (if he do not floor us and have at us by main strength); and if he let us quite alone, we are so happy of the respite we dare not make a move; but should e'er a man approach us in all honest friendship, and look upon us as fellow humans and not just a bum and a bosom, from eyes other than a stud-stallion's, and after some courteous talk should propose a cordial swiving as one might a hand of whist (instead of inviting us to whist as lecherously as though to bed)—if, I say, e'er a man should learn to make such a request in such a manner, his bed would break 'neath the weight of grateful women, and he would grow gray ere his time! But in sooth 'twill never happen," Joan concluded, "forasmuch as 'twould mean receiving a partner and not taking a vassal: 'tis not mere sport a man lusts after, 'tis *conquest*— else philanderers were rare as the plague and not common as the pox. Do but ask, Ebenezer, cordially and courteously, as ye would ask a small favor from a good friend, and what ye ask shall rarely be refused. But ye *must* ask, else in our great relief at not being hard pressed for't, we shall pass ye by."

"Indeed," admitted Ebenezer, shaking his head, "it had not struck me ere now, what a sad lot is woman's. What beasts we are!"

"Ah, well," sighed Joan, " 'tis small concern o' mine, save when I reflect on't now and again: a whore loses little sleep on such nice questions. So long as a man hath my price in his purse and smells somewhat more sweet than a tanyard and leaves me in peace come morning, I shan't say him nay nor send him off ill-pleased with his purchase. And I love a virgin as a child loves a new pup, to make him stand and beg for't, or lie and play dead. Off your knees, then, and to bed with ye, ere ye take a quartan ague from the draught! There's many a trick I'll teach ye!"

So saying she held out her arms to him, and Ebenezer, breaking at once into sweat and goose bumps from the contest between his ardor and the cold March draughts in which for a quarter hour he'd been kneeling, embraced her fervently.

"Dear God, is't true?" he cried. "What astonishment it is, to be granted all suddenly in fact what one hath yearned for time out of mind in dreams! Dear heart, what a bewilderment! No words come! My arms fail me!"

"Let not thy purse fail thee," Joan remarked, "and for the rest, leave't to me."

"But 'fore God I love thee, Joan Toast!" Ebenezer moaned. "Can it be you think yet of the filthy purse?"

"Do but pay me my five guineas ere ye commence," Joan said, "and then love me 'fore God or man, 'tis all one to me."

"You will drive me to Bedlam with your five guineas!" Ebenezer shouted. "I love thee as never man loved woman, I swear't, and rather would I throttle thee, or suffer myself throttled, than turn my love to mere whoremongering with that accursed five guineas! I will be thy vassal; I will fly with thee down the coasts of earth; I will deliver soul and body into thy hands for very love; but I will not take thee for my whore while breath is in me!"

"Ah, then, 'tis after all a fraud and deceit!" Joan cried, her eyes flashing. "Ye think to gull me with *thee*'s and *thy*'s and your prattle o' love and chastity! I say pay me my fee, Eben Cooke, or I'll leave ye this minute for ever and all; and 'tis many the hour ye'll curse your miserliness, when word of't reaches my Johnny McEvoy!"

"I cannot," Ebenezer said.

"Then know that I despise ye for a knave and fool!" Joan jumped from the bed and snatched up her garments.

"And know that I love thee for my savior and inspiration!" Ebenezer replied. "For ne'er till you came to me this night have I been a man, but a mere dotting oaf and fop;

and ne'er till I embraced thee have I been a poet, but a shallow coxcomb and poetaster! With thee, Joan, what deeds could I not accomplish! What verse not write! Nay, e'en should you scorn me in your error and ne'er look on me more, I will love thee nonetheless, and draw power and purpose from my love. For so strong is't, that e'en unrequited it shall sustain and inspire me; but should God grant thee wit to comprehend and receive it and return it as then you would perforce, why, the world would hear such verses as have ne'er been struck, and our love would stand as model and exemplar to all times! Scorn me, Joan, and I shall be a splendid fool, a Don Quixote tilting for his ignorant Dulcinea; but I here challenge thee—if you've life and fire and wit enough, love me truly as I love thee, and then shall I joust with bona fide giants and bring them low! Love me, and I swear to thee this: I shall be Poet Laureate of England!"

"Methinks thou'rt a Bedlamite already," Joan snapped, hooking up her dress. "As for my ignorance, I had rather be fool than scoundrel, and yet rather scoundrel than madman, and in sooth I believe thou'rt all three in one skin. Mayhap I'm dolt enough not to grasp this grand passion ye make such claim to, but I've mother wit enough to see when I'm hoaxed and cheated. My John shall hear of't."

"Ah Joan, Joan!" Ebenezer pleaded. "Are you then indeed unworthy? For I declare to thee solemnly: no man will e'er offer thee another such love."

"Do but offer me my rightful fee, and I'll say not a word to John: the rest o' your offer ye may put back in your hat."

"So," sighed Ebenezer, still transported, "you *are* unworthy! So be't, if't must: I love thee no less for't, or for the sufferings I shall welcome in thy name!"

"May ye suffer French pox, ye great ass!" Joan replied, and left the room in a heat.

Ebenezer scarcely noted her departure, so full was he of his love; he strode feverishly about the bedchamber, hands clasped behind his back, pondering the depth and force of his new feeling. "Am I waked to the world from a thirty-year sleep?" he asked himself. "Or is't only now I've begun to dream? Surely none awake e'er felt such dizzy power, nor any man in dreams such bursting life! *Hi!* A song!"

He ran to his writing-desk, snatched up his quill, and with little ado penned the following song:

Not Priam *for the ravag'd Town of* Troy,
 Andromache *for her bouncing Baby Boy,*
Ulysses *for his chaste* Penelope,
 Bare the Love, dear Joan, *I bear for Thee!*

But as cold Semele *priz'd* Endymion,
 And Phaedra *sweet* Hippolytus *her Step-Son,*
He being Virgin—so, I pray may Ye
 Whom I love, love my stainless Chastity.

For 'tis no niggard Gift, my Innocence,
 But one that, giv'n, defieth Recompense;
No common Jewel pluck'd from glist'ring Hoard,
 But one that, taken, ne'er can be restor'd.

Preserv'd, my Innocence preserveth Me
 From Life, from Time, from Death, from History;
Without it I must breathe Man's mortal Breath:
 Commence a Life—and thus commence my Death!

When he was done composing he wrote at the bottom of
the page *Ebenezer Cooke, Gent., Poet and Laureate of England,* just to try the look of it, and, regarding it, was pleased.

" 'Tis now but a question of time," he rejoiced. "Faith, 'tis a
rare wise man knows who he is: had I not stood firm with
Joan Toast, I might well ne'er have discovered that knowledge! Did I, then, make a choice? Nay, for there was no *I*
to make it! 'Twas the choice made *me:* a noble choice, to
prize my love o'er my lust, and a noble choice bespeaks a
noble chooser. What am I? What am I? *Virgin,* sir! *Poet,* sir!
I am a virgin and a poet; less than mortal and more; not a
man, but Mankind! I shall regard my innocence as badge of
my strength and proof of my calling: let her who's worthy
of't take it from me!"

Just then the servant Bertrand tapped softly on the door
and entered, candle in hand, before Ebenezer had a chance
to speak.

"Should I retire now, sir?" he asked, and added with an
enormous wink, "Or will there be more visitors?"

Ebenezer blushed. "Nay, nay, go to bed."

"Very good, sir. Pleasant dreams."

"How's that?"

But Bertrand, with another great wink, closed the door.

"Really," Ebenezer thought, "the fellow *is* presumptuous!" He returned to the poem and reread it several times with a frown.

" 'Tis a gem," he admitted, "but there wants some final touch. . . ."

He scrutinized it line for line; at *Bare the Love, dear* Joan, *I bear for Thee* he paused, furrowed his great brow, pursed his lips, squinted his eyes, tapped his foot, and scratched his chin with the feather of his quill.

"Hm," he said.

After some thought, he inked his quill and struck out *Joan*, setting in its place the word *Heart*. Then he reread the whole poem.

" 'Twas the master touch!" he declared with satisfaction. "The piece is perfect."

TERRY SOUTHERN

Twirling at Ole Miss

In an age gone stale through the complex of bureaucratic interdependencies, with its tedious labyrinth of technical specializations, each contingent upon the next, and all aimed to converge into a single totality of meaning, it is a refreshing moment indeed when one comes across an area of human endeavor absolutely sufficient unto itself, pure and free, no strings attached—the cherished and almost forgotten *l'art pour l'art*. Such is the work being carried forward now at the Dixie National Baton Twirling Institute, down at the campus of Ole Miss—a visit to which is well worthwhile these days, if one can keep one's wits about.

In my case, it was the first trip South in many years, and I was duly apprehensive. For one thing, the Institute is located just outside Oxford, Mississippi—and, by grotesque coincidence, Faulkner's funeral had been held only the day before my arrival, lending a grimly surreal aura to the nature of my assignment . . . namely, to get the story on the Baton Twirling Institute. Would reverting to the Texas twang and callousness of my youth suffice to see me through?

Arriving in Oxford then, on a hot midday in July, after the three-hour bus ride from Memphis, I stepped off in front of the Old Colonial Hotel and meandered across the sleepy square toward the only sign of life at hand—the proverbial row of shirt-sleeved men sitting on benches in front of the county courthouse, a sort of permanent jury.

"Howdy," I say, striking an easy stance, smiling friendly-like, "Whar the school?"

The nearest regard me in narrow surmise: they are quick to spot the stranger here, but a bit slow to cotton. One turns to another.

"What's that he say, Ed?"

Big Ed shifts his wad, sluices a long spurt of juice into the dust, gazes at it reflectively before fixing me again with gun-blue-cold eyes.

"Reckon you mean, 'Whar the school *at*?', don't you, stranger?"

Next to the benches, and about three feet apart, are two public drinking fountains, and I notice that the one boldly marked "For Colored" is sitting squarely in the shadow cast by the justice symbol on the courthouse façade—to be entered later, of course, in my writer's notebook, under "Imagery, sociochiaroscurian, hack."

After getting directions (rather circuitous, I thought—being farther put off by what I understood, though perhaps in error, as a fleeting reference to "the Till case") I decided to take a cab, having just seen one park on the opposite side of the square.

"Which is nearer," I asked the driver, "Faulkner's house or his grave?"

"Wal," he said without looking around, "now that would take a little studyin', if you were gonna hold a man to it, but offhand I'd say they were pretty damn near the same—about ten minutes from where we're sittin' and fifty cents each. They're in opposite directions."

I sensed the somehow questionable irony of going from either to the Baton Twirling Institute, and so decided to get over to the Institute first and get on with the coverage.

"By the way," I asked after we'd started, "where can a man get a drink of whiskey around here?" It had just occurred to me that Mississippi is a dry state.

"Place over on the county line," said the driver, "about eighteen miles; cost you four dollars for the trip, eight for the bottle."

"I see."

He half turned, giving me a curious look.

"Unless, of course, you'd like to try some 'nigger-pot.' "

"Nigger-pot? Great God yes, man," I said in wild misunderstanding, "let's go!"

It soon developed, of course, that what he was talking about was the unaged and uncolored corn whiskey privately made in the region, and also known as "white lightning." I started to demur, but as we were already in the middle of the colored section, thought best to go through with it. Why not begin the sojourn with a genuine Dixieland experience—the traditional jug of corn?

As it happened the distiller and his wife were in the fields when we reached the house, or hut as it were, where we were tended by a Negro boy of about nine.

"This here's a mighty fine batch," he said, digging around in a box of kindling wood and fetching out unlabeled pints of it.

The taxi driver, who had come inside with me, cocked his head to one side and gave a short laugh, as to show we were not so easily put upon.

"Why, boy," he said, "I wouldn't have thought you was a drinkin' man."

"Nosuh, I ain't no drinkin' man, but I sure know how it suppose to taste—that's 'cause times nobody here I have to *watch* it and I have to *taste* it too, see it workin' right. We liable lose the whole batch I don't know how it suppose to taste. You all taste it," he added, holding out one of the bottles and shaking it in my happy face. "You see if that ain't a fine batch!"

Well, it had a pretty good taste all right—a bit edgy perhaps, but plenty of warmth and body. And I did have to admire the pride the young fellow took in his craft. You don't see much of that these days—especially among nine-year-olds. So I bought a couple of bottles, and the driver bought one, and we were off at last for the Institute.

The Dixie National Baton Twirling Institute holds its classes in a huge, sloping, fairyland grove on the campus of Ole Miss, and it resembles something from another age. The classes had already begun when I stepped out of the cab, and the sylvan scene which stretched before me, of some seven-hundred girls, nymphs and nymphets all, cavorting with their staffs in scanty attire beneath the broadleaf elms, was a sight to spin the senses and quicken the blood. Could I but have donned satyr's garb and rushed savagely among them! But no, there was this job o'work to get on with—dry, factual reportage—mere donkey work, in fact. I decided the correct procedure was to first get some background material, and to this end I sought out Don Sartell, "Mister Baton" himself, Director of the Institute. Mr. Sartell is a handsome and personable young man from north of the Mason-Dixon line, highly intelligent, acutely attuned to the needs of the young, and, needless to say, extremely dexterous *avec les doigts*. (By way of demonstrating the latter he once mastered a year's typing course in a quick six hours—or it may have been six days, though I do recall that it was an impressive and well-documented achievement.)

"Baton twirling," he tells me straight off, "is the second largest girl's youth movement in America—the first, of course, being the Girl Scouts." (Veteran legman, I check this out later. Correct.) "The popularity of baton twirling," he explains, "has a threefold justification: (1) it is a sport which can be practiced alone; (2) it does not, unlike other solo sports (sailing, skiing, shooting, etc.), require expensive equipment; and (3) it does not, again like the aforementioned, require travel, but, on the contrary, may be practiced in one's own living room or backyard."

"Right," I say. "So far, so good, Mister Baton—but what about the intrinsics? I mean, just what is the point of it all?"

"The point, aside from the simple satisfaction of mastering a complex and highly evolved skill, is the development of self-confidence, poise, ambidexterity, disciplined coordination, etcetera."

I asked if he would like a drink of nigger-pot. He declined graciously: he does not drink or smoke. My place, I decided, is in the grove, with the groovy girls—so, limbering up my 600-page, eight-dollar copy of *Who's Who in Baton Twirling,* I take my leave of the excellent fellow and steal toward the sylvan scene below, ready for anything.

The development of American baton twirling closely parallels the history of emancipation of our women. A larger version of this same baton (metal with a knob on the end) was first used, of course, to direct military marching bands, or, prior to that, drum corps—the baton being manipulated in a fairly straightforward, dum-de-dum, up-and-down manner. The idea of *twirling* it—and finally even *flinging* it—is, obviously, a delightfully girlish notion.

Among those most keenly interested in mastering the skill today are drum majorettes from the high schools and colleges of the South and Midwest, all of which have these big swinging bands and corps of majorettes competing during the half at football games. In the South, on the higher-educational level, almost as much expense and training goes into these groups as into the football team itself, and, to persons of promise and accomplishment in the field, similar scholarships are available. Girls who aspire to become majorettes—and it is generally considered the smartest status a girl can achieve on the Southern campus—come to the Institute for preschool training. Or, if she is already a majorette, she comes to sharpen her technique. Many schools send a girl, or a small contingent of them, to the Institute to pick up the latest routines so that they can come back and teach the rest of the corps what they have learned. Still others are training to be professionals and teachers of baton twirling. Most of these girls come every year—I talked to one from Honey Pass, Arkansas, a real cutie pie, who had been there for eight consecutive years, from the time she was nine. When I asked if she would like a drink of pot, she replied pertly: *"N . . . o . . . spells 'No'!"* Such girls are usually championship material, shooting for the Nationals.

Competitions to determine one's degree of excellence are held regularly under the auspices of the National Baton Twirling Association, and are of the following myriad categories: *Advanced Solo; Intermediate Solo; Beginners Solo; Strutting Routine; Beginners Strutting Routine; Military Marching; Flag; Two-Baton; Fire Baton; Duet; Trio; Team; Corps; Boys; Out-of-State;* and others. Each division is further divided into age groups: 0-6, 7-8, 9-10, 11-12, 13-14, 15-16, 17 and over. The winner in each category receives a trophy, and the first five runners-up receive medals. This makes for quite a bit of hardware riding on one session, so that a person in the baton-twirling game does not go too long without at least token recognition—and the general run of *Who's Who* entries ("eight trophies, seventy-three medals") would make someone like Audie Murphy appear rudely neglected.

The rules of competition, however, are fairly exacting. Each contestant appears singly before a Judge and Scorekeeper, and while the Judge observes and relays the grading to the Scorekeeper, the girl goes through her routine for a closely specified time. In Advanced Solo, for example, the routine must have a duration of not less than two minutes and twenty seconds, and not more than two and thirty. She is scored on general qualities relating to her degree of accomplishment—including *showmanship, speed,* and *drops,* the latter, of course, counting against her, though not so much as one might suppose. Entrance fees average about two dollars for each contestant. Some girls use their allowance to pay it.

In the Institute's grove—not unlike the fabled Arcadia—the groups are ranged among the trees in various states of learning. The largest, most central and liveliest of these groups is the one devoted to the mastery of Strutting. Practice and instruction in Strutting are executed to records played over a public-address system at an unusually loud volume—a sort of upbeat rock and roll with boogie-woogie overtones. *Dixie, The Stripper,* and *Potato Peel* were the three records in greatest use for this class—played first at half speed, to learn the motions, then blasted at full tempo. Strutting is, of course, one of the most fantastic body-movement phenomena one is likely to see anywhere. The deliberate narcissistic intensity it requires must exceed even that of the Spanish flamenco dancer. High-style (or "all-out") Strutting is to be seen mainly in the South, and what it resembles more than anything else is a very contemporary burlesque-house number—with the grinds in and the bumps out. It is the sort of dance one associates with jaded and sequin-covered washed-out blondes in their very late thirties—but Ole Miss, as is perhaps well known, is in "the heartland of beautiful girls," having produced two Miss Americas and any number of runners-up, and to watch a hundred of their nymphets practice the Strut, in bathing suits, short shorts, and other such skimp, is a visual treat which cuts anything the Twist may offer the viewer. It is said, incidentally, that the best Strutting is done at the colored schools of the South, and that of these the greatest of all is to be seen at Alabama State Teachers College. That jazz trends have decisively influenced the style of Strutting in recent years is readily acknowledged, and is highly apparent indeed.

At the Institute, the instructor of the Strut stands on a slightly raised platform facing her class, flanked by her two assistants. She wears dark glasses, tight rolled shorts, and looks to be about 34-22-34. She's a swinger from Pensacola, Florida, a former National Senior Champion and Miss Majorette of America, now turned pro. When not at the Dixie Institute at the University of Mississippi, or a similar establishment, she gives private lessons at her own studio, for four to six dollars an hour, and drives a Cadillac convertible.

As for other, more academic, aspects of baton twirling, an exhibition was given the first evening by members of the cadre—all champions, and highly skilled indeed. It is really quite amazing what can be done with a baton, and no one could have been more surprised than your correspondent. The members of the cadre can literally walk those sticks over ever inch of the body, almost it seems without touching them. This is especially effective at night when they use a thing called the "fire baton," with a torch flaming at each end.

Instruction in speed and manipulation of this sort is a long and nerve-racking process. There is something almost insane about the amount of sheer effort and perseverance which seems to go into achieving even a nominal degree of real excellence—and practice of four hours a day is not uncommon. And yet the genuine and really impressive skill which is occasionally displayed makes it difficult to consider the art as so totally ridiculous as one would have previously believed—though, of course, another might argue that such achieved excellence only makes it more ridiculous—or perhaps not so much ridiculous as absurd. In fact, in the existentialist sense, it might well be considered as the final epitome of the absurd—I mean, people starving in India and that sort of thing, and then others spending four hours a day skillfully flinging a metal stick about. *Ça alors!* In any case it has evolved now into a highly developed art and a tightly organized movement—though by no means one which has reached full flower. For one thing, a nomenclature —that hallmark of an art's maturity—has not yet been wholly formalized. Theoretically, at least, there should be a limit to the number of possible manipulations, each of which could legitimately be held as distinct from all others—that is to say, a repertory which would remain standard and unchanged for a period of time. The art of baton twirling has not yet reached that stage, however, and innovations arise with such frequency that there does not exist at present any single manual, or similarly doctrinaire work, on the subject. Doubtless this is due in large part to the comparative newness of the art as a large and intensely active pastime—the Dixie National Baton Twirling Institute, for example, having been founded as recently as 1951. The continuing evolution of the art as a whole is reflected in the names of the various manipulations. Alongside the commonplace (or classic) designations, such as *arabesque, tour-jeté, cradle,* etc., are those of more exotic or contemporary flavor: *bat, walk-over, pretzel,* and the like . . . and all, old or new, requiring countless hours of practice.

During the twirling exhibition I fell into conversation with a couple of graduate law students, and afterward went along with them to the campus coffee shop, "Rebel Devil" or whatever it is called—nearly all shops there have the word "Rebel" in them—and we had an interesting talk. Ole Miss prides itself, among other things, on having the only law school in the state which is accredited by the American Bar Association—so that these two graduate law students were not without some claim to representing a certain level of relative advancement in the community of scholars. They were clean-cut young men in their mid-twenties, dressed in summer suits of tasteful cut. In answer to a question of mine, we talked about Constitutional Law for ten minutes before I realized they were talking about *State* Constitutional Law. When it became apparent what I was driving at, however, they were quick to face the issue squarely.

"*We* nevuh had no Negra problem heah," said one of them, shaking his head sadly. He was a serious young man wearing glasses and the mien of a Harvard divinity student. "Theah just *weren't* no problem—wasn't till these *agi-ta-tors* came down heah started all this problem business."

They were particularly disturbed about the possible "trouble, an' I mean *real* trouble" which would be occasioned by the attempted registration of a Negro student [James Meredith] which was threatening to take place quite soon, during that very summer session, in fact. As it happened, the authorities managed to delay it; I did, however, get a preview of things to come.

"Why they'll find *dope* in his room the first night he's heah," the other student said, "dope, a gun, something— *anything*, just plant it in theah an' *find* it! And out he'll go!"

They assured me that they themselves were well above this sort of thing, and were, in fact, speaking as mature and nonviolent persons.

"But now these heah young *unduh*graduates, they're hotheaded. Why, do you know how *they* feel? What *they* say?"

Then to the tune of *John Brown's Body,* the two graduate law students begin to sing, almost simultaneously: "*Oh we'll bury all the niggers in the Mississippi mud . . .*", singing it rather loudly it seemed to me—I mean if they were just documenting a point in a private conversation—or perhaps they were momentarily carried away, so to speak. In any event, and despite a terrific effort at steely Zen detachment, the incident left me somewhat depressed, so I retired early, to my comfortable room in the Alumni House, where I sipped the white corn and watched television. But I was not destined to escape so easily, for suddenly who should appear on the screen but old Governor Faubus himself—in a gubernatorial campaign rant—with about six cross-purpose facial ticks going strong, and he compulsively gulping water after every pause, hacking, spitting and in general looking as mad as a hatter. At first I actually mistook it for a rather tasteless and heavy-handed parody of the governor. It could not, I thought, really be Faubus, because why would the network carry an Arkansas primary campaign speech in Mississippi? Surely not just for laughs. Later I learned that while there is such a thing in television as a *nation*wide hookup for covering events of national importance, there is also such a thing as a *South*wide hookup.

The Institute's mimeographed schedule, of which I had received a copy, read for the next day as follows:

7:30	Up and at 'em
8-9	Breakfast—University Cafeteria
9-9:30	Assembly, Limber up, Review—Grove
9:30-10:45	Class No. 4
10:45-11:30	Relax—Make Notes
11:30-12:45	Class No. 5
1-2:30	Lunch—University Cafeteria
2:30-4	Class No. 6
4-5:30	Swim Hour
6:30-7:30	Supper—University Cafeteria
7:30	Dance—Tennis Court
11	Room Check
11:30	Lights Out (No EXCEPTIONS)

The *"Up and at 'em"* seemed spirited enough, as did the "No EXCEPTIONS" being in heavy capitals; but the rest somehow offered little promise, so, after a morning cup of coffee, I walked over to the library, just to see if they really had any books there—other than books on Constitutional Law, that is. Indeed they did, and quite a modern and comfortable structure it was, too, air-conditioned (as was, incidentally, my room at the Alumni House) and well-lighted throughout. After looking around for a bit, I carefully opened a mint first-edition copy of *Light in August,* and found "nigger-lover" scrawled across the title page. I decided I must be having a run of bad luck as, a few minutes later, I suffered still another minor trauma on the steps of the library. It was one of those incredible bits of irony which sometimes do occur in life, but are never suitable for fiction—for I had completely put the title-page incident out of my mind and was sitting on the steps of the library, having a smoke, when this very amiable gentleman of middle age paused in passing to remark on the weather (102°) and to inquire in an oblique and courteous way as to the nature of my visit. An immaculate, pink-faced man, with pince-nez spectacles attached by a silver loop to his lapel, nails buffed to a gleam, he carried a smart leather briefcase and a couple of English-literature textbooks which he rested momentarily on the balustrade as he continued to smile down on me with what seemed to be extraordinary happiness.

"My, but it's a mighty warm day, an' that's no lie," he said, withdrawing a dazzling white-linen handkerchief and touching it carefully to his brow, ". . . an' I expect you all from up Nawth," he added with a twinkle, "find it especially so!" Then he quite abruptly began to talk of the "natural tolerance" of the people of Mississippi, speaking in joyfully objective tones, as though it were, even to him, an unfailing source of mystery and delight.

"Don't mind nobody's business but yoah own!" he said, beaming and nodding his head—and it occurred to me this might be some kind of really weirdly obscured threat, the way he was smiling; but no, evidently he was just remarkably good-natured. " 'Live an' let live!' That's how the people of Mississippi feel—always have! Why, look at William Faulkner, with all his notions, an' him livin' right ovah heah in Oxford all the time an' nobody botherin' him—just let him go his own way—why we even let him teach heah at the University one yeah! That's right! I know it! Live an' let live—you can't beat it! I'll see you now, you heah?" And his face still a glittering mask of joviality, he half raised his hand in good-by and hurried on. Who was this strange, happy educator? Was it he who had defaced the title page? His idea of tolerance and his general hilarity gave one pause.

I headed back to the grove, hoping to recover some equilibrium. There, things seemed to be proceeding pretty much as ever.

"Do you find that your costume is an advantage in your work?" I asked the first seventeen-year-old Georgia Peach I came across, she wearing something like a handkerchief-size Confederate flag.

"Yessuh, I *do*," she agreed, with friendly emphasis, tucking her little blouse in a bit more snugly all around, and continuing to speak in that oddly rising inflection peculiar to girls of the South, making parts of a reply sound like a question: "Why, back home near Macon . . . Macon, Georgia? At Robert E. Lee High? . . . we've got these outfits with *tassels!* And a little red-and-gold skirt? . . . that, you know, sort of *flares out?* Well, now they're awful pretty, and of course they're *short* and everything, but I declare those tassels and that little skirt get in my way!"

The rest of the day passed without untoward incident, with my observing the Strut platform for a while, then withdrawing to rest up for the Dance, and perhaps catch the Faub on video again.

The Dance was held on a boarded-over outdoor tennis court, and was a swinging affair. The popular style of dancing in the white South is always in advance of that in the rest of white America; and, at any given moment, it most nearly resembles that which is occurring at the same time in Harlem, which is invariably the forerunner of whatever is to become the national style. I mused on this, standing there near the court foul line, and (in view of the day's events) pursued it to an interesting generalization: perhaps *all* the remaining virtues, or let us say, positive traits, of the white Southerner—folk song, poetic speech, and the occasional warmth and simplicity of human relationships—would seem rather obviously to derive from the colored culture there. Due to my magazine assignment, I could not reveal my findings over the public-address system at the dance—and, in fact, thought best to put them from my mind entirely, and get on with the coverage—and, to that end, had a few dances and further questioned the girls. Their view of the world was quite extraordinary. For most, New York was like another country—queer, remote, and of small import in the scheme of things. Several girls spoke spiritedly of wanting to "get into television," but it always developed that they were talking about programs produced in Memphis. Memphis, in fact, was definitely the mecca, yardstick and *summum bonum*. As the evening wore on, I found it increasingly difficult, despite the abundance of cutie pieness at hand, to string along with these values, and so finally decided to wrap it up. It should be noted too, that girls at the Dixie National are under extremely close surveillance both in the grove and out.

The following day I made one last tour, this time noting in particular the instruction methods for advanced twirling techniques: *1-, 2-, 3-finger rolls, wrist roll, waist roll, neck roll,* etc. A pretty girl of about twelve was tossing a baton sixty feet straight up, a silver whir in the Mississippi sunlight, and she beneath it spinning like an ice skater, and catching it behind her back, not having moved an inch. She said she had practiced it an hour a day for six years. Her hope was to become "the best there is at the high toss and spin"—and she was now up to seven complete turns before making the catch. Was there a limit to the height and number of spins one could attain? No, she guessed not.

After lunch I packed, bid adieu to the Dixie National and boarded the bus for Memphis. As we crossed the Oxford square and passed the courthouse, I saw the fountain was still shaded, although it was now a couple of hours later than the time before. Perhaps it is always shaded—cool and inviting, it could make a person thirsty just to see it.

JAMES PURDY

Don't Call Me by My Right Name

Her new name was Mrs. Klein. There was something in the meaning that irritated her. She liked everything about her husband except his name and that had never pleased her. She had fallen in love with him before she found out what his name was. Once she knew he was Klein, her disappointment had been strong. Names do make a great difference, and after six months of marriage she found herself still not liking her name. She began using more and more her maiden name. Then she always called herself on her letters Lois McBane. Her husband seldom saw the mail arrive so perhaps he did not know, and had he known she went by her old name he might not have cared enough to feel any particular hurt.

Lois Klein, she often thought as she lay next to her husband in bed. It is not the name of a woman like myself. It does not reflect my character.

One evening at a party when there had been more drinking for her than usual, she said offhand to him in the midst of some revelry: "I would like you to change your name."

He did not understand. He thought that it was a remark she was making in drink which did not refer to anything concrete, just as once she had said to him, "I want you to begin by taking your head off regularly." The remark had meant nothing, and he let it pass.

"Frank," she said, "you must change your name, do you hear? I cannot go on being Mrs. Klein."

Several people heard what it was she said, and they

laughed loudly so that Lois and Frank would hear them appreciating the remark.

"If you were all called Mrs. Klein," she said turning to the men who were laughing, "you would not like to be Mrs. Klein either."

Being all men, they laughed harder.

"Well, you married him, didn't you," a man said, "and we guess you will have to keep his name."

"If he changed his name," another of the men said, "what name would you have him change it to?"

Frank put his hand on her glass, as though to tell her they must go home, but she seized the glass with his hand on it and drank quickly out of it.

"I hadn't thought what name I did want," she said, puzzled.

"Well, you aren't going to change your name," Frank said. "The gentlemen know that."

"The gentlemen do?" she asked him. "Well, I don't know what name I would like it changed to," she admitted to the men.

"You don't look much like Mrs. Klein," one of the men said and began to laugh again.

"You're not friends!" she called back at them.

"What are we, then?" they asked.

"Why don't I look like Mrs. Klein?" she wanted to know.

"Don't you ever look in the mirror?" one of the men replied.

"We ought to go, Lois," her husband said.

She sat there as though she had heard the last of the many possible truths she could hear about herself.

"I wonder how I will get out of here, Frank," she said.

"Out of where, dear?" he wondered. He was suddenly sad enough himself to be dead, but he managed to say something to her at this point.

"Out of where I seem to have got into," she told him.

The men had moved off now and were laughing among themselves. Frank and Lois did not notice this laughter.

"I'm not going to change my name," he said, as though to himself. Then turning to her: "I know it's supposed to be wrong to tell people when they're drunk the insane whim they're having is insane, but I am telling you now and I may tell the whole room of men."

"I have to have my name changed, Frank," she said. "You

know I can't stand to be tortured. It is too painful and I am not young anymore. I am getting old and fat."

"No wife of mine would ever be old or fat," he said.

"I just cannot be Mrs. Klein and face the world."

"Anytime you want me to pull out is all right," he said. "Do you want me to pull out?"

"What are you saying?" she wanted to know. "What did you say about pulling out?"

"I don't want any more talk about your changing your name or I intend to pull up stakes."

"I don't know what you're talking about. You know you can't leave me. What would I do, Frank, at my age?"

"I told you no wife of mine is old."

"I couldn't find anybody now, Frank, if you went."

"Then quit talking about changing our name."

"*Our* name? I don't know what you mean by *our* name."

He took her drink out of her hand and when she coaxed and whined he struck her not too gently over the mouth.

"What was the meaning of that?" she wanted to know.

"Are you coming home, Mrs. Klein?" he said, and he hit her again. Her lip was cut against her teeth so that you could see it beginning to bleed.

"Frank, you're abusing me," she said, white and wide-eyed now, and as though tasting the blood slightly with the gin and soda mix.

"Mrs. Klein," he said idiotically.

It was one of those fake dead long parties where nobody actually knows anybody and where people could be pushed out of windows without anybody's being sure until the morrow.

"I'm not going home as Mrs. Klein," she said.

He hit her again.

"Frank, you have no right to hit me just because I hate your name."

"If you hate my name what do you feel then for me? Are you going to act like my wife or not?"

"I don't want to have babies, Frank. I will not go through that at my age. Categorically not."

He hit her again so that she fell on the floor, but this did not seem to surprise either her or him because they both continued the conversation.

"I can't make up my mind what to do," she said, weeping a little. "I know of course what the safe thing is to do."

"Either you come out of here with me as Mrs. Klein, or I go to a hotel room alone. Here's the key to the house," he said, and he threw it on the floor at her.

Several of the men at the party had begun to notice what was really going on now. They thought that it was married clowning at first and they began to gather around in a circle, but what they saw had something empty and stiff about it that did not interest and yet kept one somehow watching. For one thing, Mrs. Klein's dress had come up and exposed her legs, which were not beautiful.

"I can't decide if I can go on with his name," she explained from the floor position to the men.

"Well, it's a little late, isn't it, Mrs. Klein," one of the men said in a sleepy voice.

"It's never too late, I don't suppose, is it?" she inquired. "Oh, I can't believe it is even though I feel old."

"Well, you're not young," the same man ventured. "You're too old to be lying there."

"My husband can't see my point of view," she explained. "And that is why he can't understand why his name doesn't fit me. I was unmarried too long, I suppose, to suddenly surrender my own name. I have always been known professionally and socially under my own name and it is hard to change now, I can tell you. I don't think I can go home with him unless he lets me change my name."

"I will give you just two minutes," Mr. Klein said.

"For what? Only two minutes for what?" she cried.

"To make up your mind what name you are going out of here with."

"I know, men," she said, "what the sensible decision is, and tomorrow, of course, when I'm sober I will wish I had taken it."

Turning to Frank Klein, she said simply, "You will have to go your way without me."

He looked hurriedly around as though looking for an exit to leave by, and then he looked back to her on the floor as though he could not come to a decision.

"Come to your senses," Frank Klein said unemphatically.

"There were hundreds of Kleins in the telephone directory," she went on, "but when people used to come to my name they recognized at once that I was the only woman going under my own special name."

"For Jesus Christ's sake, Lois," he said, turning a peculiar green color.

"I can't go with you as Mrs. Klein," she said.

"Well, let me help you up," he said.

She managed to let him help her up.

"I'm not going home with you, but I will send you in a cab," he informed her.

"Are you leaving me?" she wanted to know.

He did not know what to say. He felt anything he said might destroy his mind. He stood there with an insane emptiness on his eyes and lips.

Everyone had moved off from them. There was a silence from the phonograph and from the TV set which had both been going at the same time. The party was over and people were calling down to cabs from all the windows.

"Why won't you come home with me?" she said in a whisper.

Suddenly he hurried out the door without waiting for her.

"Frank!" she called after him, and a few of the men from the earlier group came over and joked with her.

"He went out just like a boy, without any sense of responsibility," she said to them without any expression in her voice.

She hurried on out too, not waiting to put her coat on straight.

She stood outside in the fall cold and shivered. Some children went by dressed in Hallowe'en costumes.

"Is she dressed as anybody?" one of the children said pointlessly.

"Frank!" she began calling. "I don't know what is happening really," she said to herself.

Suddenly he came up to her from behind a hedge next to where she was standing.

"I couldn't quite bring myself to go off," he said.

She thought for a minute of hitting him with her purse which she had remembered to bring, but she did nothing now but watch him.

"Will you change your name?" she said.

"We will live together the way we have been," he said, not looking at her.

"We can't be married, Frank, with that name between us."

Suddenly he hit her and knocked her down to the pavement.

She lay there for a minute before anything was said.

"Are you conscious?" he said crouching down beside her. "Tell me if you are suffering," he wanted to know.

"You have hurt something in my head, I think," she said, getting up slightly on one elbow.

"You have nearly driven me out of my mind," he said, and he was making funny sounds in his mouth. "You don't know what it means to have one's name held up to ridicule like this. You are such a cruel person, Lois."

"We will both change our names, if you like," she said.

"Why do you torture me?" he said. "Why is it you can't control your power to torture?"

"Then we won't think about it, we will go home," she said, in a cold comforting voice. "Only I think I am going to be sick," she warned.

"We will go home," he said in a stupid voice.

"I will let you call me Mrs. Klein this one evening, then tomorrow we will have a good talk." At the same moment she fell back on the walk.

Some young men from the delicatessen who had been doing inventory came by and asked if there was anything they could do.

"My wife fell on the walk," he said. "I thought she was all right. She was talking to me just a moment ago."

"Was it your wife, did you say?" the younger man leaned down to look at her.

"Mrs. Klein," Frank replied.

"You are Mr. Klein, then?"

"I don't understand," the older of the two young men said. "You don't look somehow like her husband."

"We have been married six months."

"I think you ought to call a doctor," the younger man said. "She is bleeding at the mouth."

"I hit her at a party," Frank said.

"What did you say your name was?" the older man asked.

"Mr. Klein. She is Mrs. Klein," Frank told them.

The two men from the delicatessen exchanged looks.

"Did you push her?" the one man asked.

"Yes," Frank said. "I hit her. She didn't want to be Mrs. Klein."

"You're drunk," the one man ventured an opinion.

Lois suddenly came to. "Frank, you will have to take me home," she said. "There is something wrong with my head. My God," she began to scream, "I am in awful pain."

Frank helped her up again.

"Is this your husband?" the one man asked.

She nodded.

"What is your name?" he wanted to know.

"It's none of your business," she said.

"Are you Mrs. Klein?" he asked.

"No," Lois replied, "I don't happen to be Mrs. Klein."

"Come on, J. D., we can't get mixed up in this," the younger man said. "Whatever the hell their names are."

"Well, I'm not Mrs. Klein, whoever you are," she said.

Immediately then she struck Frank with the purse and he fell back in surprise against the building wall.

"Call me a cab, you cheap son of a bitch," she said. "Can't you see I'm bleeding?"

CONRAD KNICKERBOCKER

Pay Day

"Call me doctor," my old man would bellow as he charged through the door on Saturday night, his eyes like chipped hardboiled eggs. I learned to spend Sundays in a ten-cent Mexican movie house, the Rio Rita. I'd come home and find Pappy hunkered down in a wash tub, wallowing and groaning in cracked ice, and my mother in the kitchen, pounding away at a fifty-pound chunk. He was different. He thought you froze out a hangover. He said steam baths after a drunk bloated the liver, "engorging it in a rush of fetid and ill-humored blood."

Let's be brief, he was a nut. We had come down in the world, as Father Muldoon used to say before he quit nodding to us on the street. Amid the splinters of his farm-boy room, Pappy had read *Dr. Jekyll and Mr. Hyde*. His calling came clear to him then, and he only thirteen. But instead of Buchner funnels, Gooch crucibles, potash bulbs and burettes, he had to settle for antacids, condoms, and powdered douches. In the red plastic briefcase he claimed he had found on a bus, he stored his diploma from a pharmacological school, now defunct, in Little Rock; assorted licenses that he somehow managed to keep current; and the prize certificate, a diploma from the College of Astral Knowledge of Cincinnati, granting him the degree of Doctor of Alchemical Philosophy. D. Aph.

If I came too close during his therapy, he'd sail a handful of ice at me and yell, "You little self-abuser, you'll ruin us all with your peeping-tom tricks." If I forgot to look in on him, he'd lob the ice piece by piece into the toilet, then off to bed. In the next few days, he'd try to make it up, restore optimism all around, winking and snuffling, bouncing his coffee on the saucer for emphasis, spinning nickels through the air whenever the smell of horse and the tired loping sound of bells announced that the Meadow Gold ice-cream wagon was underneath our windows. "I'm on to it now, boy. It won't be long now," he'd say.

"It" being the life work, the quest, as he put it, for the modern philosopher's stone. The Jekyll-and-Hyde syndrome still had him. He was bursting with information, muttering about the *prima materia* and the virtue of white non-corrosive sulphur, until if he could have found a salamander he would have been up roasting it all night.

"But they were on the wrong track," he later admitted. I guess he meant Albertus Magnus and Rhazes and Vincent of Beauvais and whoever else had him hipped at the time. Those names I knew better than the Cardinals' that year. "No sir, boy, they should have looked for the 'stone' (chemical, my lad, heh-heh) that will give us all the gold of the glorious life and the spirit. Not, young fellow, the GOLD OF THE MARKET PLACE!" Bang. Down would come the fist. The Jello would lunge across the table and my mother would look at her lap. Until another Saturday night rolled around and it was time for the Rio Rita again.

He worked the prescription counter nights at a Torpedo drugstore at the foot of Quality Hill, in that neon patch of shoe-shine parlors, novelty shops and taverns around the Rasbach hotel. The other pharmacist on duty (the custom in rubbers was brisk) always read *Liberty* and the final edition of the *Star*, but not Pappy. He was deep in *De Mineralibus*, borrowed from the public library on a Saturday afternoon before he began swilling his usual twelve boilermakers at the Hula Hut bar. He was disgusted with modern pharmacology and despised the pensioners and widows who pushed their grubby prescriptions at him. The more sophisticated the medicine, the angrier he got. The barbiturates were "poison, a scourge." The jolly faddish blendings of dexadrine and Amytal would "send the human race back to the jungle."

"No, young fellow," he would say, scratching under his undershirt, "people don't need to be held down. They'll find true peace only when they connect with the Astral Spirit, the Great Hand of the Universe. We must find the way to release them from their mortal envelope."

I would nod empty-eyed, my mind full of the rayon-encased breasts of Grace Emerick and Judy McCoy and best of all, June Bug Shotwell. That spring I was sixteen and the sap ran free. Boobies were all the philosophy I needed, but Pappy couldn't abide my vacant nose-picking.

"Someday you'll thank your lucky stars you were the son of an educated man," he would shout, slapping clouds of dust out of a gold-edged book.

He eventually denounced the alchemists, "brave but benighted." His real loves were the great magicians, the star frauds, rascals, prison breakers and crystal-gazers of the ages. Dr. John Dee was an old friend, and he grumbled that he would not have the opportunity to meet the Comte de St. Germain in this life. He read *The Magus or Celestial Intelligencer* constantly. He was on speaking terms with the five Infernal Kings of the North, Sitrael, Palanthan, Thamaar, Falaur, and Sitrami. He recited to himself in a singsong whisper, swinging his foot in a circle over the end of the brown horsehair divan:

> The serpents of the Hermetic caduceus
> entwine three times; Cerberus opens
> his triple jaw, and fire chants the
> praises of God with the three tongues
> of the lightning.

All of this was harmless enough. The talk about Appolonius of Tyana and adepthood kept him going. Life was a merry round of suppositories, hocus-pocus and the Hula Hut. Then one Saturday afternoon while he was poking around the stacks of the library, coughing and swatting at the books that were out of line, he stumbled onto the works of Dr. Wilhelm Reich. It was a bad day for us. Pappy, once he saw the true light, began to crumble fast. Dr. Reich's orgone theories happened to jibe with the work he was doing on a mage he particularly admired, Aleister Crowley, The Great Beast 666. All the mysterious happenings at the Abbey of Thelema came clear to him in a flash.

"The Great Beast was after the same thing," he announced. "You're too young to know anything about this. Acts of ritual sex magic . . ," he would mumble off.

He began to patronize a Chinese grocery store on the other side of town. He pilfered powders from the drugstore and spent hours in the bathroom, mixing and chanting to himself. His reading became ferocious. He dragged home pharmacopoeias and was up all night glaring at them. "Those old boys were onto something," he declared while he snuffled over *Thoth the Hermes of Egypt*. Pharmacodynamics and orgone metaphysics were the supper table talk. The monologues got longer, he got meaner and his job at Torpedo suffered. For three years, he had managed to hang on there despite his drinking and a suspicious squint. The store was soot-laden, but it enabled us to live in an apartment with three rooms, hot and cold water included, over a tavern on the leeward side of the stockyards. The manager of the Torpedo store was a man named Gladfeld, a toothless hulk who ate ten Baby Ruths a day. He wasn't having any of Pappy's latest daydreams. He began circulating rumors. He whispered to the higher-ups at Torpedo headquarters that Pappy had bad habits, that he liked to be alone a lot, that he didn't perform his family duties. Even the delivery boy started snickering. Pappy said customers were staring at him and pretty soon he looked as though he actually did prefer pocket pool.

The crisis came when one of the soda fountain girls commented to him one day, "My, you look pale! And those trembly hands!"

That did it. He couldn't face it any longer. He resigned. Somewhere he got the idea that his fellow workers were scheming to circulate a petition against him.

To pursue his life work, he had even given up his Saturday nights for awhile. But after he left the job, he went back to them hammer and tongs. My mother got a job as a short-order cook and Pappy hung around the library and the Hula Hut. At school that spring, I had been a member of the Boy Scouts and the safety patrol, happy that Pappy was dispensing syringes behind the worn but solid counter at Torpedo, but when he quit, I began to see the folly of it all. No more merit badges.

I guess I was responsible in a way for the trouble that followed. I was supposed to go to a free camp for ten days near Sedalia, but instead I burrowed as deep as I could into the heart of the stockyards district. If we were going down, I wanted to know where we were headed. My tennis shoes stuck in the soft tar of the streets, but I liked the hopeless brown railroad buildings, the stench and the background rustle of animal movements. One July day I looked up after a concentrated study of a three-legged fice dog worrying a sick rat in an alley and saw for the first time Cermag's drugstore across the street, standing there improbable and gaunt in the sunlight. I wandered through the dark door. A little man, sleek and moist as a shoat, came out from the gloomy shelves.

"No punks in here," he said as though he had said it many times before. He was much older than I thought.

"I'm not a punk. I need a job. I'll clean up, deliver and jerk sodas."

"Sodas, hah! You got a work permit?"

"Yes." This wasn't true.

"Here." He shoved a broom at me. "Let's see how you sweep."

I swept furiously, kicking up a mushroom cloud of dust. After a couple of hours and more palaver he hired me for the summer, twelve hours a day, fifteen cents an hour. The store was a collection of shelf after shelf and stack after stack of obsolete proprietaries dating back to 1873. A moldy fountain with four stools ran down one side. Cermag's trade involved a horde of Poles who worked down the street at the John Weitershen and Sons packing house two blocks away, popping in for cigars, snuff, railroad caps, and licorice. An occasional young cowboy from Mankato, Kans., or Cozad, Nebr., came in for a bag of Bull Durham and then ambled over to a tottering house across the street. These were the boys who told me that the place was in fact a whore house, something I had never seen before.

The whore house was majestic, with broken stained-glass windows, varicose brick, and a mudline from the flood of '03 running about twelve feet up. The front porch sagged and peeled, but it had a wooden swing that would seat three girls at one time. Sometimes they would come across the street for a Dr. Pepper. Mainly they ordered bottles of sweet soda to mix with their sloe gin. The lady in charge had asthma, and she waddled in occasionally to giggle while Cermag fixed her up with a pack of Cubebs.

Cermag had a man with a waxed mustache working for him. "Pharmacist," Cermag declared, but I never saw him fill a prescription. The fellow spent most of his time huddled with truck drivers on street corners. One day he failed to show up.

"Your father still out of work?" Cermag asked me. I

nodded, struck dumb at what I knew was coming next.

"Tell him around here come." Cermag talked like that sometimes. One of the Poles told me the old man had been an officer in the Serbian army during the 1914-18 war but was cashiered and had to leave the country. He had written lewd notes to one of the ladies-in-waiting attached to what was left of the royal family. I once asked Cermag where he was from. "Cuba," he said and barked his doggy laugh.

My getting a job had thrown Pappy into a funk. We seldom spoke. That particular morning, the stench of the packing house was thick in my dreams as I awoke. I heard him banging his shoe against the wall in the other room, a habit he'd picked up to frighten the mice. The night before I'd told him about the vacancy at Cermag's. One bead of sweat had dripped from his bony nose, but he hadn't said a word. Somewhere down the street a dog now howled, impossible, a wild joke at that time of day. I yelled, "Shut up!" and pulled the pillow over my head.

All became silent, a terrible calm. I should have known better, but to be sure the dog could hear me, I yelled again. Pappy dropped his shoe on the floor and the bed springs squealed. I realized my error and reached for my pants, but it was too late. He shot through the door.

"You young bastard," he began. "You leech. What do you mean by telling me to shut up? Ah Christ, Ah God, all these years I've put up with your tricks, and now this!"

"But Pappy, I was yelling at the dog."

"What dog?" He wasn't having any of it. He paused a moment. Then he rushed to my dresser and swept it clean with his fist. Bottles, pictures, comb, brush, part of a peanut butter sandwich flew across the room. "What dog?" he bellowed. He smashed his fist against the wall and a rain of plaster descended from the ceiling. He picked up a bottle of Lucky Tiger and flung it out the window. He was breathing hard now. "I'll show you dog," he howled. He pulled out a drawer from the bureau and heaved it across the room. Handkerchiefs, my two clean shirts, and a sock flew out of it. Pappy reeled out of the room and collapsed onto the horsehair sofa. He panted for five minutes. Finally he squinted at the wall. "Take me to this Cermag," he said.

They got along like long-lost brothers. Within a day they were whispering together in the back room. A week of confabulations went by. At the end, a path was cleared through the rubbish on the prescription counter, and pieces of chemical apparatus began to gleam on the pocked wood. Pappy had found a patron.

It started with a few beakers and retorts. A Bunsen burner began hissing all day long. Finally a device he called a Soxhlet extractor loomed over the rest of the glassware. Then came the ingredients of whatever it was Pappy and Cermag were cooking up. Pappy lugged in books by the armful. Dust danced everywhere. He called them off and Cermag wrote them down—asoka, mugwort, caperberry, euphorbium, avena sativa, cardoon, bhang.

"Bhang," Cermag intoned, "is hemp."

"Get it," Pappy begged. "Look, it says right here . . ."

Cermag shrugged and joined the truckdrivers on the corner, and in a day the work continued. Pappy loomed like a huge fish through the flasks and bottles. He became beneficent again, just as in the Torpedo days.

"We've got it, boy, we've got it," he sang as the apparatus rumbled. "From all this will come the stone that will blow humanity right out of their mortal envelopes onto the astral plane."

The day of the stone arrived. Arm in arm, Cermag and Pappy surveyed a small pile of grey material heaped like lumpy cement on a copy of *The Police Gazette*. They ground this business in a mortar and encapsulated it in gelatin. It all ended up in a brown bottle that Cermag hid somewhere in back of the store.

"Now for the test," Pappy rubbed his hands together. They got their chance that afternoon when one of the regulars, Vladimir Wisniowiecki, a tremendous lout, totally bald, with a chest like a vat, wandered in for a plug of Horseshoe.

"You don't look so good, Vlad," Cermag confided.

"Vot? Vot?" Vladimir bellowed, all good nature. His grin was overpowering.

"You don't look so good, I said. Come back here. I fix you up."

The Pole moved like a tank to the back of the drugstore. Pappy and Cermag started into the spiel. I could catch phrases like "orgone imbalance" and "sexual stasis." Wisniowiecki stood scratching his head. Finally he dug a dollar bill out of the hammer pocket in his bib overalls. The brown bottle appeared. The Pole clasped the pill in his hand as if he were carrying a time bomb and scurried across the street.

Two hours later he was back, grinning and triumphant. "It vork just like you say. It vork!" He did some kind of polka on the pustular linoleum and danced out in the direction of the packing house. Pappy and Cermag began to dance themselves.

"I've done it! The astral plane!" Pappy cackled.

"One buck a pill. Those insane Polacks," Cermag agreed.

At that moment, a girl appeared in the doorway. The cowboys had pointed her out before. It was Jeannie, recognizable from afar by the smallness of her ankles and the enormity of her bosom. She was the star of the place. Some said she was working here only long enough to save money and to win the clientele for a place of her own.

"What the hell did you give that dumb bohunk?" she shouted. "He nearly killed me!"

"Here," I said, churning up a root-beer float with a flourish. "This will revive you." She slumped at the counter and drank it without a word.

In the days that followed, she became a steady customer, permitting me to deliver Camels and handpacked fudge-ripple ice cream as far as the parlor of the house. "You're too young," she would say, but it seemed to me her eyes lingered. Meanwhile, the drugstore had become all business. Vladimir apparently had passed the word, and at first three or four of his fellow health-addicts had shown up to have their orgone balance restored, then a dozen, then finally what appeared to be the entire work force of John Weitershen and Sons.

Pay days were worst. Those giant beef luggers, pork trimmers, meat grinders and intestine stuffers poured into the store, stamping their feet and cracking the cigar-counter glass. It was all we could do to hold them in line while Cermag went through the ritual of prescribing for each. The moment they received their pills, off they would go, itching, burning up, throwing their money in all directions as they stampeded up the steps of the house. It was ghastly. They became maniacs. They foamed and raved and trampled everything in their path, cats, dogs, the little Mexican kids on their way to the river. A cowboy told me the girls had begun to work in shifts. It couldn't go on.

The time soon came when the pills were nearly gone. Pappy began to set up his equipment again, but Cermag stopped him. "I can't go through all that mess and boiling again," he said. "This time, we'll give them sugar."

"Sugar!" Pappy was outraged. "This isn't one of your cheap, shoddy swindles. This is THE ART OF HEALING!"

"Healing, hell. We'll use sugar."

That night my father barely ate his supper. He poked at his Jello, sighing and shaking his head. He locked himself in the bathroom for a couple of hours and flushed the toilet frequently. In between the shudders of the plumbing, I could hear his shoe heel tapping on the wall.

The next morning proved Cermag was right. Vladimir came in for a treatment, and Cermag slipped him a sugar capsule and stuffed the dollar bill into those baggy pants of his. "There, it fix you up," he said in benediction. Usually, Vladimir returned in a couple of hours with a success story, but this time he failed to show up. Perhaps it was too hot. Pappy was terrified, however.

"He's on to us, I know it," he whimpered. The old man shrugged.

"Tomorrow is pay day," Cermag replied, and his face took on that smooth, blubbery look that came when he was thinking about money.

Pay day bloomed with heat. I was up and out of the apartment early. Pappy hadn't slept well, and when he was afraid, he was liable to go off on one of those frenzies so hard on the furniture. When I arrived at the store, I sat down on a soda-fountain stool and waited for Cermag to finish putting out the magazines. He straightened up suddenly and gave me the needle eye.

"Where's the broom?" he asked. I couldn't answer him. How should I know where the broom was? If I'd found it, I'd have wrapped it around his neck. "Get the broom," he said, "and push it. Watch the store. When your father comes, tell him I'm across the street." Out he went into the blinding morning, like a rabbit. With his sudden affluence, he'd taken to visiting the house once a week, but only in the morning, "when the girls are fresh," he explained.

In the cool dark of the store I settled down in the decaying easy chair behind the prescription counter. Old magazines were piled everywhere, dusty and already fading, heaped in with empty bottles and boxes. I picked up a magazine: *Movie Confessions*—impossible, no genuine bodies, nothing but a mass of lies. I was about to dig really deep into the pile of junk when suddenly my chair seemed to explode and I was on the floor breathing the rotten wood. A jug of lemon syrup began to thud down the basement steps one at a time.

When I finally focused my eyes again, there was Pappy, brandishing the broom like a baseball bat. "The big day," he roared, "and you want to play with yourself. You are RUINING MY LIFE WORK!" He aimed the broom at me again, this time in pool-cue fashion as though he were going to sink me in the far pocket.

I always mumbled and stuttered in situations like this, but I was desperate; he had me cornered. "Pappy," I began, "Vlad . . ."

"Vlad what?" He waved the broom closer to my head. From the floor, he looked as tall as a Watusi.

Suddenly, a vast light dawned. Inspiration had left me before, but it came now. "The Poles are on to your tricks," I blurted. "They're coming after you and Cermag with meat hooks."

The broom descended slowly and Pappy's expression began to flake away. He stood immobile for a moment, and then was all arms and legs as he began moving off in every direction.

"I'll fix you later. Now get Cermag." He started running up and down the length of the store, piling magazines against the plate-glass window at the front. He was making a barricade, ready to fight to the death. When he couldn't find any more magazines, he started in on the cartons of old Odorono bottles and jars of Mother Onegin's White Root ointment, huffing and blowing, bent double. The window looked like a junk yard. I raced across the street and up the steps of the house. Inside we found Cermag working himself into a lather with one of the girls. He had her on his lap, tickling her, twittering and prodding. I didn't have time for games. "Cermag," I began, "Pappy is falling apart . . ."

"Out, out," he shot at me. "Back to the store. You're too young for this kind of thing. They'll put you in an institution if they catch you hanging around here." That was too much. I let him have it straight between the eyes. "Pappy says the Poles know about the sugar," I said. "They're going to skin you alive."

"What do you mean? What do you mean?" His mouth

popped open. He jumped up and the girl tumbled to the floor in a flurry of lace and blue-white flesh.

"The plant closed early today and the Poles heard you're going to sugar their pills. There'll be a riot. You don't stand a chance," I told him.

"My God," he said. "Holy Mother of God, they'll kill me." He threw his arm around my neck and we bolted from the house.

Out in the street we heard occasional shouts, bursts of song, rumbles and banging. Cermag muttered that he smelled blood in the air. The noise seemed to come closer by the second as we whisked across the street. Now the window was filled with debris of every kind. My father had discovered a mattress somewhere and it was lying at the top of the crazy barricade. We tried the front door. Pappy had locked it. We hammered and pounded and kicked, but it was no use. He must have thought we were the enemy. He wouldn't budge; he didn't make a sound. He was ready to let us have it with every weapon he could lay his hands on. If I knew Pappy, he was roasting, teeth bared, dancing around a case of horse liniment. We yelled and kicked some more, but the door was like a tombstone.

Cermag was frantic. He realized that Pappy would probably heave the entire stock at us—ten-year-old mustard plasters, cream-soda bottles and all—if we so much as showed our faces. We had to figure a better way to get in, but by this time it was already too late. As Cermag prepared to jimmy the lock with his pen knife, a torrent heaved into sight. They were singing some cracked Polish anthem, bellowing it, improvising on it in full harmony. They didn't look dangerous to me, but Cermag's knees dissolved at the sound. "Help me," he whimpered. "My heart's gone. I'm done for."

In the sunlight his face seemed to be melting away, and I almost believed him for a moment, but then it struck me that the old lecher was trying to pull a disappearing act, and I whacked him across the back a couple of times. I wasn't finished with him yet. "That'll fix your heart," I said. He took me seriously. He straightened up and gave the door a shattering kick. It hesitated and squeaked, but the game was up. The Poles had reached the store and were straining at the side of the building. We were engulfed, caught up and thrown about in the flood, bobbed to and fro, battered and squeezed, suffocated. The din was terrifying. I couldn't make myself heard. They swarmed over us, their hands full of money. They were ravenous, on fire. I had never seen them quite this way before. They packed the street, and they were singing that song even more loudly. One of them near me quit shouting long enough to ask me why we didn't open up. I knew the fellow. He was the bane of the house across the street, an athlete of the worst kind. I told him we had lost the keys and couldn't get in. He passed the word to his friends and soon all of them knew what to do. They quit singing and let out a real war cry.

No door was going to stop them. They wanted the pills so badly that many of them turned scarlet, steam pouring from their bodies, boiling from exertion and the heat. They swept me aside and gathered themselves up for the grand charge. The whole mob catapulted into the front of the building. A great fog of dust rose into the air. The store tottered a little. It creaked, it moaned, but the window still stood unbroken, a miracle. The Poles were baffled. No flesh had ever withstood them before, and to be stopped by a mere door was too much. The girls in the house now leaned out of the windows and egged on their patrons in a frenzy of joy. They danced and screamed. They stripped themselves naked and flung it all—panties, stockings, chemises—into the pandemonium below. The army took heart. They grabbed at the cloud of flimsies. In a convulsion of lust, they waved the garments as battle flags.

At that moment, Wisniowiecki's great moon face appeared in a window between two of the fatter girls. "Hey, Cermag," he yelled, and a hush fell on the mob. "Hey, good pill today. You good doctor." A roar went up. Dollar bills filled the air. The girls cackled.

Cermag was sitting on the curb a block away. He had given up. He wasn't even listening any more, squatting there, his face in his hands.

Pappy wasn't a man to be caught napping, as he often said. Sure enough, just before the Poles could attack again, the door popped open and he appeared for an instant, his arms full of cans of hair straightener. He fired them into the mob with the speed of a machine gun. Panic-stricken, the horde turned tail and ran.

The girls burst into an eruption of screeching and braying, insults and taunts. Ashamed, the Poles rallied and formed themselves into a tight and lethal ball on the opposite side of the street. All became quiet. Even the whores gave up their thunder for the moment. Before Pappy could bring up more ammunition, the entire herd stampeded into the store front. The facade of the building exploded with a final crack. Boards and pieces of glass hailed down on the pavement, and a plume of soot and dust spiraled sedately toward the sky. The roof teetered and sagged and part of the timbers began to tumble into the pit below. I caught a glimpse of an old bathtub before it crashed down with the rest of the wall. The girls screamed with ecstasy. It looked as though they were about to throw themselves from the windows. Not a Pole was in sight. They had completely disappeared into the yawning shell of the building. Cloud on cloud of junk vomited from what was left of the doorway, and a caterwauling promised that the back wall would probably collapse under the assault at any moment.

I couldn't stand it any more. I walked down the gutter to where Cermag was sitting and nudged his backside with my toe. "Maybe we can save some of the stock," I said. He looked up at me for a moment, his face streaked with dirt, his eyes wet. He didn't say a word.

One by one the Poles clambered out of the wreckage. They were covered with dust and foot powder. Enema kits festooned their necks and they wore ice cream on their faces like war paint.

Like weary soldiers who have captured the opposing standards, they feebly waved flags of aged toilet paper. They crammed their pockets with old laxative bottles, cans of shoe polish, tubes of denture adhesive. One brandished a plumber's helper like a war club. It was the Fall of Constantinople all over again. They were completely unmanned, with barely enough strength to drag themselves along after their orgy. They passed the house without glancing upward. The girls were stupefied. They leaned out of the windows, gaping at their former champions. Soon, they left the windows of their rookery, to retire, no doubt, exhausted to their beds. The street fell silent again. In the immense heat we could hear our own breathing.

But not for long. A police car suddenly appeared from nowhere, its siren wailing. The car stopped, and a fat cop emerged, smoking a corncob pipe. I nudged Cermag again, but we were both too weak to move. The sight of that gigantic destruction had left us without the strength to lift a finger. If the cop had threatened to shoot us on the spot, we couldn't have budged. He spied us and ambled over, his feet as big as gunboats.

"My God," he said. "What did this?"

I pondered a moment. "The trucks did it. These trucks drive by for years and shake the buildings. Eventually a place falls down. That's all," I said.

The cop took the pipe out of his mouth and spat on the pavement. "I've heard of that," he said finally. "Anybody hurt?"

Suddenly I remembered and felt a surge of happiness. "My father, he's buried alive!" I shouted and ran toward the pit of junk. The cop lumbered after me.

"We'll be back," he yelled. He drove off. I picked up a board and poked listlessly at the mountain of magazines and lumber. Cermag remained seated on the curb. For all I knew or cared, he'd turned to lead.

In a few minutes a fire engine pulled up and a horde of firemen jumped off circus style, armed to the teeth with axes and shovels. They launched a ferocious attack on the wreckage, churning it up, trampling and rolling in it, reducing the whole works to a fine powder. They were worse than the Poles. They shouted obscene encouragements to one another. They screamed with zeal when they uncovered a new and fairly solid piece of junk. They leaped on it, shoveling and hacking away at it until it was pulverized. The girls in the house dressed themselves and came out to watch. They had found a new clientele. After the debacle, there'd be treats all around.

A car with a press sign in the window drew up and several photographers and reporters piled out. They set up their equipment, a collection of sagging tripods and gadgets, and began clicking away at the firemen. A reporter came over to me and asked what it was all about. "The trucks did it," I told him.

"Hell with that," he said. "Who set off the bomb?"

I told him that Pappy was buried in the mess, just to give him something to think about. He was astounded. He grabbed me by the arm and dragged me over to the spectacle. "Here," he said, handing me one of the firemen's shovels, "start digging. 'Youth Finds Father's Body in Blast Wreckage.'" He was in rapture.

I piddled away at the junk while the cameras buzzed. I tried to look earnest. I saw Jeannie in the crowd and waved. She smiled back at me, now that I was a public figure. Then I spotted a quivering pink patch in the dust. I dug a little further and revealed Pappy's head. A great hooray went up from the crowd. When I uncovered that bald dome of his, I felt like telling them they'd made a mistake. It was disgusting. I dug some more and revealed his ears, his nose, his mouth. Finally I reached his chin line and gave up. The thought of uncovering him inch by inch was too much to take. I knew he wasn't dead. He knew it too. He opened one eye and, unblinking, stared at us all. I threw down my shovel and the firemen started to dig the rest of him out.

Wisniowiecki emerged from the house, amiable and immense, spreading the crowd before him like the prow of a ship. When he saw Pappy buried to the neck in that mountain of rubble, he paused, marveling.

"Where is drugstore?" he asked. "Never mind," he said, digging into his overalls and pulling out a crumpled five-dollar bill. "We got plenty these. You go to another store, make more pills, hah?"

A photographer, a man with a head like a suitcase, asked me, "How'd you spell that last name again?"

Just then a girl's voice called, "Hey, hero." I turned around. It was Jeannie. She was calling to me. "Hey, hero, come on." Vlad continued to gape, waving the money. I grabbed the bill from him and elbowed my way to Jeannie. Hand in hand we ran across the street to the house.

"H-E-R-O," I yelled back at the photographer. "HERO SHIMA!"

"Hiroshima who?" he called.

We paused on the porch. Their cameras were aimed at me. Pappy's eye had caught the sun and seemed to be the largest lens of all.

"Knock-knock, you sons of bitches," I yelled through cupped hands and we went inside.

LOUIS-FERDINAND CELINE

from Journey to the End of the Night

I was dropped by the quacks in the end and was able to keep my hide intact, but I'd been branded now for good. There was nothing to be done about it. "Get out," they said. "You're no longer any good at all."

"I'll go to Africa," I said to myself. "The further away I go, the better." It was a Corsair Line boat which took me on board. It was headed for the tropics, like all the company's other boats, with a cargo of cotton goods, officers and colonial administrators.

So old was the boat that they'd taken away the brass plate on the upper deck which had the date of its birth on it; that had been so very long ago it would have given rise to apprehension, as well as jokes, among the passengers.

They put me on this boat, then, for me to go and try to make a new man of myself in the colonies. They wished me well and were determined that I should make my fortune. Personally I only wanted to get away, but as one ought always to look useful if one isn't rich and as, anyway, my studies didn't seem to be getting me anywhere, it couldn't very well last. I hadn't enough money to go to the States, though. So "Africa has it," I said, and I let myself be hounded towards the tropics where I was told you only had not to drink too much and to behave fairly well to make your way at once.

These prognostications made me think. There weren't many things to be said in my favour, but it was true that I bore myself decently and quite well. I was deferential, and always frightened of not being in time, and careful never to get ahead of any one in life; in fact, I was polite.

When one's been able to escape alive from a mad international shambles, it says something after all for one's tact and discretion. But about this voyage. While we stayed in European waters, things didn't seem likely to go too badly. The passengers squatted about the lower decks, the lavatories and the smoking room in suspicious, drawling little groups. The whole lot of them were soaked in *amer picons* and gossip from morning till night. They belched, snoozed and shouted by turns and never seemed to regret having left Europe at all.

Our ship was called the *Admiral Bragueton*. She could only have floated on these steamy seas thanks to the paint on her hull. So many coats of paint had been laid one on top of the other on her hull that the *Admiral Bragueton* had a sort of second skin, like an onion. We were cruising towards Africa; the real, vast Africa of limitless forests, dangerous swamps, unbroken solitudes, where negro kings squatted amid a network of unending rivers. For a packet of Pilett blades they were going to barter fine long pieces of ivory with me, and birds of bright plumage and slaves under age. That's what I'd been promised. I was going to really live, so they told me. I'd have nothing in common with this Africa, innocent of all agencies, public monuments, railways and tins of toffee. There'd be nothing of that sort. Oh, no! We were going to see Africa in the raw, the real Dark Continent, we bibulous passengers on board the *Admiral Bragueton.*

But when we were past the coast of Portugal, things began to go wrong. One morning we woke up to find ourselves overcome by a breathless sort of stove atmosphere, disquieting and frightful. The drinking water, the sea, the air, the sheets, our own sweat, everything was warm, sticky. From then onwards it was impossible, by day or by night, to feel anything cool in one's hand, under one's bottom, down one's throat, but the ice in the whiskey served at the ship's bar. An ugly despair settled on the passengers on board the *Admiral Bragueton;* they were condemned never to leave the bar, dripping, clinging to the ventilators, grasping little bits of ice, threatening each other after bridge and incoherently apologizing.

It didn't take long. In this maddeningly unchanging temperature the whole human freight of the ship clotted together in one vast tipsiness. People walked wanly about the deck, like jellyfish at the bottom of a pool of stagnant water. It was then that one saw the whole of the white man's revolting nature displayed in freedom from all constraint, under provocation and untrammelled; his real self as you saw it in war. This tropic stove brought out human instincts in the same way as the heat of August induces toads and vipers to come out and flatten themselves against the fissured walls of prison buildings. In the cold of Europe, under prudish northern fogs, except when slaughter is afoot, you only glimpse the crawling cruelty of your fellow men. But their rottenness rises to the surface as soon as they are tickled by the hideous fevers of the tropics. It's then that the wild unbuttoning process begins, and degradation triumphs, taking hold of us entirely. A biological confession of weakness. As soon as work and the cold restrain us no longer, as soon as their stranglehold is loosened, you catch sight in the white race of what you see on a pretty beach when the tide goes out; reality, heavy-smelling pools of slime, the crabs, the carcasses and scum.

And so when Portugal was passed, every one on the boat began, ferociously, to give vent to their instincts: they were helped in this by alcohol and that comfortable feeling, best known to soldiers and officials in service, which comes of not having to pay one's fare. To feel that for a month on end one is being given food, drink and one's bed free and for nothing is enough in itself, you'll agree, to make one rave with delight at such economy. I, the only paying fare on board, was considered, as soon as the fact became known, extraordinarily bad-mannered, a quite intolerable bounder.

If, when we left Marseilles, I had had any experience of colonial society, I should have gone on bended knee, in my unworthiness, to ask pardon and mercy of that colonial infantry-officer, the highest in rank on board, whom I was continually meeting everywhere about the ship. And perhaps I should have prostrated myself also, to make assurance doubly sure, at the feet of the oldest civil servant. Then do you think these fantastic travellers would have tolerated my presence among them without unpleasantness? But, in my ignorance, my unthinking claim to be allowed to breathe the same air as they very nearly cost me my life.

One is never fearful enough. As it was, thanks to a certain

skillfulness on my part, I lost nothing but what was left of my self-respect.

And this is the way things happened.

Some time after passing the Canary Islands, I learnt from a steward that I was generally looked upon as a *poseur*, not to say an insolent fellow. That I was suspected of pimping, not to mention pederasty . . . of taking cocaine as well, a bit. . . . But that only as a side line. . . . Then the notion got about that I'd had to make my escape from France following certain very grave offences against the law. Even so, I was only at the beginning of my trials. It was then that I found out about the practice usual on this line of never taking paying passengers except with extreme circumspection, and of subjecting to as much ragging as a new boy gets at school all passengers who did not travel free, either on a military pass or thanks to some bureaucratic arrangement, since French colonies actually belong, as is well known, to the élite of the government departments.

After all, there aren't many valid motives which might induce an unknown citizen to venture in this direction. . . . I was a spy, a suspect; a thousand reasons were found for cold-shouldering me, the officers averting their eyes, the women with a meaning smile. Soon the stewards themselves were encouraged by this to exchange heavily caustic remarks behind my back. In the end no one doubted at all that I was really the nastiest and most intolerable dirty dog on board— the only one, in fact. It was a fine lookout.

At table, I sat next to four toothless, liverish, postal officials from the Cameroons. At the beginning of the voyage they had been familiar and friendly; now they didn't address a single word to me. By tacit accord I was being sent to Coventry and closely watched by every one. I no longer left my cabin, except with extreme caution. The boiling atmosphere weighed down on us as if it were solid. Naked, behind my locked door, I lay quite still and tried to imagine what plan these devilish people might have devised to be rid of me. I knew no one on board, yet every one seemed to know me. My description must have become well-known, photographed in their minds, like that of a famous criminal published in the Press.

Without wishing it, I had begun to take the part of the necessary "infamous unworthy wretch," the scorn of humanity, pointed at through the centuries, familiar to every one, like God and the Devil, but assuming always a different shape, so fugitive on earth and in life as to be actually indefinable. To pick out this wretch, to seize on him and identify him, exceptional conditions had been needed, such as only existed on our restricted hulk.

A general moral rejoicing was imminent aboard the *Admiral Bragueton.* This time the evil-eyed one wasn't going to get away with it. And that meant me. The event in itself was enough to make the voyage ' worth while. Surrounded by these people who chose to be my enemies, I tried as best I might to identify them without their knowing it. To this end I spied on them with impunity, especially in the morning, through the porthole of my cabin. Before breakfast, in pyjamas and transparent against the light, covered with hair from their eyebrows to their navels and from the small of their backs to their ankles, my enemies came out to enjoy the morning coolness or sprawled against the side and roasted, glass in hand, threatening to vomit at any minute—especially the captain with his bulging, blood-shot eyes, whose liver troubled him from dawn. Regularly every morning he asked after me from the other buffoons, wanting to know if I'd been "flung overboard" yet. "Like a lump of dirty phlegm!" To add point to his remarks, he spat into the viscous sea. A hell of a joke.

The *Admiral Bragueton* made hardly any headway: she seemed to drag herself along, grunting between each roll. It was an illness now, a voyage no longer. The members of this morning council of war, as I examined them from my coign of vantage, all seemed to me pretty seriously stricken with some disease or other—malaria, alcoholism, syphilis probably. Their decay, which I could see at ten yards' range, consoled me somewhat for my own personal worries. After all, they were beaten men, like me, these fire eaters! They were arrogant still; that was the only difference! The mosquitoes had already started in to suck their blood and fill their veins with poisons which cannot be got rid of. . . . Gonococci by this time were filing away their arteries. . . . Alcohol was eating up their livers. . . . The sun was cracking their kidneys. . . . Crabs had fastened in their hair and eczema covered their stomachs. . . . The blazing light would eventually dim their retinas. . . . In a little while what would they have left? A few scraps of brain. . . . What could they do with that? I ask you . . . where they were bound for. Commit suicide?

It wouldn't be of any use to them where they were going except to help them commit suicide, in the places they were headed for. Whatever you may say, it's no fun growing old in countries where there are no distractions. . . . Where one has to look at oneself in a glass which is itself decaying, filming over. . . . You rot quick enough in green places, especially when it's hideously hot.

The North will at least preserve your flesh for you; Northerners are pale for good and all. There's very little difference between a dead Swede and a young man who's had a bad night. But the Colonial is full of maggots the day after he gets off the boat. That's just what these infinitely industrious larvæ have been waiting for, and they won't let him go till long after life is over. A crawling carcass, that's all he is.

We'd eight more days at sea before touching at Bragamance, our first taste of the promised land. I felt as if I were living in a case of high explosives. I hardly ate at all, so as not to have to meet these people in the saloon, or cross their decks in daylight. I didn't open my mouth. I was never seen walking about. It was difficult to be as small as I was and still remain on the boat.

My cabin steward, who was a family man, kindly informed me that our fine upstanding colonial officers had sworn, with glasses raised, to slap my face at the first opportunity and then to throw me overboard. When I asked him why, he said he hadn't any idea and himself asked me what I had done for things to come to such a pitch. We were left in doubt on this point. . . . It might go on a long time. I was a cad, that's all there was to it.

They'd never again get me to travel in the company of people who were so hard to please. They had so little to do, what's more, shut up alone with themselves for a whole month, that it needed very little to make them angry. If it comes to that, one may as well realize that in everyday life at least a hundred people thirst for your miserable life in the course of a single ordinary day—all those people, for instance, whom you annoy by being ahead of them in the Underground queue; all the people who pass by your apartment and haven't one of their own; all those who would like you to hurry up and come out of the lavatory so that they can go in there themselves; your children too, and a host of others. It goes on all the time. One gets accustomed to it. On board ship this friction is more easily noticeable, so it's more annoying.

In this bubbling stewpot, the grease exuded by these human ingredients becomes concentrated; a presentiment of the frightful loneliness which in the colony is going soon to engulf them and their hopes for the future, makes them groan already like dying men. They clutch, bite, scratch, ooze. My importance on board increased prodigiously from one day to the next. My rare appearances in the saloon, however furtive and silent I strove to make them, had now become events of real significance. As soon as I came in, a hundred passengers gave a single start and began whispering.

The colonial officers at the captain's table, primed with *apéritifs*, the tax collectors, and the governesses from the Congo (of which we had a fine selection on board the *Admiral Bragueton*) had endowed me with an infernal importance by jumping from malicious suppositions to slanderous conclusions. When we'd embarked at Marseilles, I was little more than an insignificant dreamer: now, owing to the venomous concentration of these alcoholic males and unsatisfied females, I had been brought unrecognisably and unpleasantly into the limelight.

The captain, a shady fellow, cunning and covered with warts, who when the voyage began had gladly enough shaken me by the hand, now when we met seemed no longer to recognise me; he avoided me as one avoids a wanted man actually guilty of some crime. . . . Guilty of what? When there's no risk attached to hating people, stupidity quickly discovers conviction; motives spring up ready-made.

As far as I could make out in the serried ranks of antagonism pitted against me, there was one young governess who led the feminine element of the cabal. She was going back to the Congo to die—at least, I hope so. She was hardly ever separated from the colonial officers, resplendent in their gorgeous tunics and armed with the oath they had sworn that they would annihilate me, as if I were some infectious insect, long before our next port of call. It was widely debated whether I should be more unpleasant flattened out than I was alive and kicking. In fact, I was a source of entertainment. This young lady spurred them on, invoked the wrath of Heaven on my head, wouldn't rest till I had been picked up in pieces, until I'd paid the penalty for my imaginary offence in full, been punished indeed for existing and, thoroughly beaten, bruised and bleeding, had begged for mercy under a rain of blows and kicks from the fine fellows whose pluck and muscular development she was aching to admire. Deep down in her wasted insides, she was stirred at the thought of some magnificently blood-bespattered scene. The idea of it was as exciting to her as that of being raped by a gorilla. Time was slipping by and it is unwise to keep the arena crowd waiting. I was the victim. The whole ship clamoured for my blood, seemed to tremble from keel to rigging in expectation.

The sea kept us fast in this floating circus. Even the stokers knew what was afoot. And as there were only three days more before we berthed—three decisive days—several executioners volunteered their services. And the more I avoided the fracas, the more aggressive and threatening towards me every one became. Those about to perform the sacrifice were getting their hand in. My cabin was sandwiched between two other cabins at the end of a cul-de-sac. I had escaped hitherto by the skin of my teeth, but it was becoming downright dangerous for me to go along to the lavatories. So now that there were only three more days, I decided definitely to renounce all Nature's needs. The porthole was enough for me. A weight of hatred and boredom bore down on everything around me. It certainly is an unbelievable boredom on board a ship—a cosmic boredom. It covers the whole sea, the boat and the sky. Even reasonable people might be driven to wild excesses by it, let alone these unreal savages.

A sacrifice! A sacrifice! I wasn't going to be allowed to escape it. Things came to a head one evening after supper, when I'd felt too hungry to resist going to the saloon. I'd kept my nose down over my plate, not daring even to bring out a handkerchief to mop the sweat from my face. Nobody has ever eaten more unobtrusively than I did. A small regular throb came up under one's seat from the engines as one ate. My neighbours at the table must have known what had been decided about me, because they began, to my surprise, to talk to me about duels and swordplay, pleasantly and at length, and to ask me questions. At that moment too, the Congo governess—the one whose breath smelt so strongly—entered the lounge. I had time to notice that she was wearing a spectacular lace evening gown; with nervous haste she went over to the piano and played, if one can call it playing, a number of airs, all of which she left unfinished. The atmosphere had become extremely sinister and tense.

Like a shot, I bolted back towards the refuge of my cabin. I'd almost reached it when one of the officers, the greatest swaggerer and the toughest of them all, barred my way resolutely, but without violence. "Let's go up on deck," he enjoined me. We were there in no time. He was wearing for the occasion his most gold-braided képi, and had buttoned up his tunic from top to bottom, which he hadn't ever done since the voyage began. So we were to have full dramatic ceremonial, evidently. I didn't amount to much; my heart was thumping somewhere about the level of my navel.

Such unusually formal preliminaries suggested a slow and painful execution of sentence. The man seemed to me like a further fragment of the war confronting me again, purposeful, murderous, inescapable.

At the same time, drawn up behind him, very much on the alert, four junior officers blocked the companionway, forming an escort to Fate.

There was no way out. The harangue which followed must have been meticulously thought out. "Sir, you are in the presence of Captain Frémizon of the Colonial Service. In the name of my fellow officers and of the passengers on this ship, all of whom are justly indignant at your outrageous behaviour, I have the honour to demand an explanation from you. We consider intolerable certain remarks which you have made about us since you came aboard at Marseilles. Now is the time for you, sir, to air your grievances aloud, to repeat openly the shameful things you have been whispering these past three weeks—to say, in fact, whatever you may have to say for yourself!"

I was immensely relieved when I heard these words. I had feared a summary execution of some sort, but they offered me, in that the captain was talking to me, a means of escape. I seized this ray of hope. Any chance of cowardice is a wonderful possibility of salvation if you know what you're up to. That's what I thought. Never quibble about how to escape being gutted, nor lose time in puzzling out the reasons for a persecution directed against oneself. Escape in itself is enough, if one is wise.

"Captain!" I said to him in as confident a voice as I could just then muster. "You are making an extraordinary mistake! Me of all people! And you, Captain! How *can* such disloyal feelings be attributed to me? Really, it is too unfair! The very thought of it dumbfounds me. . . . How *can* they? I, who but the other day was fighting for our country! I, whose blood with your own has flowed in so many unforgettable battles! What an injustice you are heaping upon me, Captain!"

Then, addressing myself to the whole group, I went on: "Gentlemen, what is this appalling slander which has deceived you all? How can you have dreamt that I, your brother in arms, could ever descend to spreading monstrous rumours about gallant officers of the army! It is too much; really it is too much. . . . And that I should choose to do so at just such a time when, brave men one and all, they're going out again to guard, loyally to guard, our immortal Colonial Empire! That Empire in whose service the foremost soldiers of our race have covered themselves with eternal glory—the Mangins, the Faidherbes, the Gallienis! Oh, Captain, that such things should be said of man!"

I broke off and waited. I hoped to have impressed them. Fortunately I had, for one short moment. With no loss of time, therefore, I took advantage of this truce and their confusion and, going right up to him, seized both his hands with a fine show of emotion.

I felt better with his hands firmly clasped in mine. Never letting go of them, I went on volubly explaining my position, and while I assured him that he'd been entirely in the right, I said that we must make a fresh start, he and I, this time getting things quite straight between us. That my understandable if foolish timidity was alone responsible for this fantastic dislike that had been taken to me. That my behaviour might indeed very well have been considered extraordinary and arrogant by this group of ladies and gentlemen, "my gallant and charming fellow travellers. . . . Luckily they were people of character and understanding. . . . And many of the ladies were marvellously musical, an ornament to the society on board!" I made an honourable and profuse apology and wound up by begging them to admit me without the least suspicion or reserve into the heart of their happy company of patriots and brothers. . . . I wished them to like me henceforth and always. . . . I didn't let go of his hands, of course, but I redoubled my eloquence.

When not actually busy killing, your soldier's a child. He's easily amused. Unaccustomed to thought, as soon as you talk to him he has to make terrific efforts in order to understand what you're saying. Captain Frémizon wasn't engaged in murdering me, he wasn't drinking either, he wasn't doing anything with his hands, or with his feet: he was merely endeavouring to think. It was vastly too much for him. Actually I had him mentally overcome.

Bit by bit, while this humiliating trial lasted, I felt my self-respect, which was about to leave me anyway, slipping still further from me, then going completely and at last definitely gone, as if officially removed. Say what you like, it's a very pleasant sensation. After this incident I've always felt infinitely free and light; morally, I mean, of course. Perhaps fear is what you need most often in life to get you out of a hole. Personally, since that day I've never myself wanted any other weapon, or any other virtues.

The captain was at a loss, and his fellow officers, who had come there for the purpose of smashing me and scattering my teeth about the deck, now had to put up with mere words scattered in the air instead. The civilians, who'd also come rushing at the news of an execution, glowered unpleasantly. As I wasn't quite certain of what I was saying (except that I stuck for all I was worth to the lyric note) I gazed straight ahead at a given spot in the soft fog, through which the *Admiral Bragueton* was wending her way, wheezing and slobbering at every stroke of her propeller. At last, to conclude my speech, I risked waving one arm above my head, and letting go of one of the captain's hands to do so, only one, I came to an impressive close:

"Among soldiers and gentlemen, should any misunderstanding be allowed to exist? Long live France, then, in God's name! *Vive la France!*" It was Sergeant Branledore's gambit. And it worked on this occasion too. That was the only time my country saved my life; till then, it had been quite the reverse. I noticed my audience hesitate for a second; but after all, it's very difficult for an officer to strike a civilian in public, however ill-disposed towards him he may feel, just when the other is shouting *"Vive la France!"* as loudly as I had then. Their hesitation saved me.

I grasped two arms at random in the group of officers and invited everybody to come along to the bar and drink to my health and our reconciliation. The gallant fellows hung back only for a moment; then we drank for two hours. But the females on board watched us silently and in slowly growing disappointment. Through the portholes I watched the piano-playing governess obstinately prowling up and down, with several lady passengers, like a hyena. They guessed, the bitches, that I'd slipped out of the ambush by a ruse, and they meant to catch me again on the rebound. All this while, we men went on drinking under the useless and maddening electric fan which, since we left the Canaries, had feebly churned an air like warm cotton. But I had to keep in form, I had to start the ball rolling again, so as to please my new friends, making things easy and pleasant for them. I never ran dry of patriotic admiration, wary of slipping; I went on and on asking these heroes one after another for more and more stories of colonial feats of arms. War stories are like the dirty variety; they never fail to please all soldiers of all nationalities. What you really need to make a sort of peace with these men, whether they're officers or privates—a fragile armistice it's true, but nevertheless very valuable—is, whatever happens, to let them expand and bask in idiotic self-glorification. Intelligent vanity does not exist. It's merely an instinct. Yet there is no man who is not vain before all else. One human being can only tolerate another human being and rather like him, if he plays the part of an admiring door-mat. I didn't have to do any mental hard work with these military gentlemen. It was enough never to stop seeming amazed and delighted. And it's easy to ask for more and more war stories. My young friends simply bristled with them. I could have imagined myself back in the good old hospital days. At the end of each of their anecdotes I did not forget to show my appreciation, in the way I'd learned from Bran-ledore, with a fine phrase. "That's something that deserves to go down to History!" As a formula, it's as good as they make them. The circle I had so stealthily squeezed my way into began bit by bit to consider me an interesting fellow. They began to say many things about the war as wildly absurd as those I had heard in the old days and later invented myself, when competing imaginatively with my mates in hospital. Of course, their setting was different; their fantasies wandered at large in the forests of the Congo instead of in the Vosges or in Flanders.

My good Captain Frémizon, the one who earlier had assumed the task of purifying the boat of my disgusting presence, began, now that he had noticed my habit of listening more attentively than any one else, to show me the more charming side of his character. His arteries seemed to be softened by my novel expressions of admiration, his vision cleared, those bulging, bloodshot eyes that betrayed the confirmed toper finally even sparkled, despite his brutishness, and the few little doubts as to his own worth which may have assailed him still whenever he was very depressed, were now adorably dispersed for a time by my marvellously intelligent and pertinent comments.

By Gad, I was the fellow to make a party go! They slapped their thighs in approbation. No one else could make life so enjoyable in spite of the moist horror of these latitudes. The point is that I was listening beautifully.

While we were carrying on in this way, the *Admiral Bragueton* began to go slower still; she slowed down in her own juice. Not a breath of air stirred about us; we were hugging the coast and doing it so slowly that we seemed to be shifting through molasses.

Syrupy too was the sky above the decks, nothing but a black, deep paste which I gazed at hungrily. To get back into the night was what I wanted most of all, to get back there, sweating and groaning or any way, it didn't matter how. Frémizon never stopped talking. Land seemed quite close but my plan of escape filled me with deep anxiety. . . . Little by little our talk ceased to be military and became jaunty, then frankly smutty, and at last so downright dirty that it was hard to know how to keep it going. One after another my guests gave up the attempt and fell asleep, and were shaken by snores, unpleasant slumber grating in their noses. Now or never was the time to get away. It's no good wasting these intervals of kindness which nature somehow manages to impose on even the most vicious and aggressive of earthly creatures.

We were at anchor just then, not far from land. All you could see of it were a few lanterns waving along the shore.

Very quickly a hundred swaying canoes full of chattering black men came alongside. These natives swarmed all over the ship, offering their services. In no time I was at the gangway with the few bundles into which I had furtively made up my things, and streaked off behind one of the boatmen, whose face and movements in the darkness I could hardly see. At the bottom, down by the water slapping the ship's side, I wondered where we were going.

"Where are we?" I asked him.

"At Bambola-Fort-Gono," the shadow answered.

We pushed off into the open, paddling hard. I helped him, so as to increase our speed.

In my flight I caught one more glimpse of my dangerous companions on board. Under the lights between decks I could see them, overcome, comatose and gastric, still twitching and grunting in their sleep. Bloatedly sprawling, they all looked the same now, all these officers, civil servants, engineers and traders, mingling, swarthy, spotted, guzzling. A dog looks like a wolf when he's asleep.

In a few minutes I had reached land once more and had found the night as well. It was thickest under the trees and there for me too, beyond the night itself, was all the complicity of silence.